INDUCTION : Some Current Issues

INDUCTION:

Some Current Issues

PAPERS BY

W. Ross Ashby, Daniel E. Berlyne, Richard B. Braithwaite,
Adolf Grünbaum, Norwood Russell Hansen, Hughes Leblanc,
Sidney Morgenbesser, Herbert Robbins,
and Wesley C. Salmon

COMMENTS AND DISCUSSION BY

Max Black, Robert S. Cohen, Richard C. Jeffrey, William Kessen,
Henry E. Kyburg, Jr., Michael Scriven, Paul L. Shiman,
and others

EDITED BY

Henry E. Kyburg, Jr., *and* Ernest Nagel

WITH AN INTRODUCTION BY MR. NAGEL

Wesleyan University Press

MIDDLETOWN, CONNECTICUT

Library of Congress Catalog Card Number: 63-8860
Printed in the United States of America
First Edition

Contents

Foreword

THIS collection of essays and conversations are the edited proceedings of a meeting held at Wesleyan University, during the week of June 12–17, 1961, sponsored by the Center for Advanced Study at Wesleyan and by the International Union of History and Philosophy of Science, Division of Logic, Methodology, and Philosophy of Science.

To judge by the comments we have received since the conference ended, this was not only a successful meeting but a fruitful one. Not long ago, a scholar asked us in skeptical tones if we really thought such a conference could bear any fruit, if we really thought that any of the protagonists changed their minds in the course of argument. We had to admit that the major protagonists—those with well-developed and well-defined points of view—were not likely to abandon their views during a five-day conference. But we had two rejoinders which satisfied the critic and may perhaps satisfy others who are somewhat doubtful (as who is not?) of the utility of conferences. The rejoinders are these: First, those who profit most definitely and most directly from such a conference as this one are not the writers of the major papers. They are the younger and less well-known participants. The development of the young masters is promoted to a high degree by taking part in—and even by witnessing—the conflicts of the old masters. Second, the writers of the major papers are not completely insulated from the criticism they evoke. One cannot expect a point of view which has been twenty years in the forming to be overthrown by a few comments at a meeting; but points of view change in time, and the sum of these comments can have a profound effect on the further development of that point of view over a period of time.

None of this justifies the publishing of a book containing the essays and comments produced by the conference, though it fully justifies the conference itself. The book must stand on its own merits. Certainly there can be no doubt that the publication of the major papers is valuable. They are good papers by good people, we think, and on a subject which, important though it is, has not been "collected" nearly as much as other subjects have been.

The comments on the papers and the replies to the comments (where these exist), certainly enhance the value of the papers. They do this in three ways. First, of course, the comments and replies clear away confusions and misunderstandings; often matters which are obscure in the original paper will be picked up and clarified. Second, the comments and replies will generally focus on some central issue in the paper being discussed, and will thus often help the reader to be alert to the issues that are alive and important. Finally, they give the reader a chance to watch two good minds at work on the same issue, and to observe the dialectic of living philosophers and scholars. Philosophers are flesh and bones; they are in error sometimes, and sometimes they make mistakes—even quite trivial ones. And it is a healthy thing, we think, that the reader not only observe the intellectual prowess, but also have the opportunity to see the human frailties, of these men.

It is with this in mind that we are also presenting summaries of the discussions to which each day's official activity was largely devoted. It would be exciting if we could capture the spirit of this conference through summaries of the discussions. But so much of the spirit was in the unofficial gatherings and discussions that took place at mealtimes and cocktail hours and late at night that we cannot hope to do this. What we can do is attempt to give a veridical impression of both the intellectual content and the intellectual temper of the official discussions.

The discussions that follow each of the papers in this volume are slightly fictitious. We have allowed our sense of suitability to modify our reports of the discussions not only for the sake of brevity but for the sake of clarity. In order to play fair with the reader, it will be well for us to explain precisely how the reports of the discussions arose and how they were modified.

The major papers at the conference were written and distributed to the participants ahead of time. They were not read at the meetings. Each meeting opened with a statement by the author of the paper to be discussed, summarizing his paper. This was followed in turn by a prepared criticism of the paper, and an unprepared rebuttal of the criticism by the author of the paper. The floor was then opened for general discussion. The papers appear here essentially as they were distributed. The summaries and rebuttals were edited by the author of the paper after the conference; the final form of the commentary was prepared by the commentator after the conference. During the discussions one or two of the participants were asked to take notes. These notes form the basis of what is presented here. We have submitted the notes, in their raw form, to the participants of the conference, and invited their corrections and emendations, deletions, and additions. We have occasionally changed the notes from *oratio obliqua* to *oratio recta*. We have made deletions of our own, and alterations of phrasing where the alterations have brought the text closer to the spirit of the discussion. We have attempted to make every unclear reference clear; and we have added material from the tape recordings that were made during each meeting. We have also tried to remain true to the character of the discussions by not imposing criteria of relevance that were too strict; these criteria, after all, are our criteria; and what strikes us as irrelevant may, in some cases, not strike someone else as irrelevant at all. In short, we have tried, without rewriting the script entirely, to reconstitute the sense of the discussions in as intelligible a way as possible.

The editors confidently speak for the participants of the conference in expressing their gratitude to the Center for Advanced Study of Wesleyan University and to the International Union for the History and Philosophy of Science for making the conference possible. We are also indebted to Wesleyan University for subsidizing the publication of this book.

Many individuals contributed freely of their time and effort to make the conference a success. Mrs. Morton W. Briggs dealt efficiently with quantities of correspondence during the early stages of the conference; Mrs. Baxter S. Patrick, Mrs. Pat Sutherland, and Mrs. C. Hess Haagen cut stencils and saw to the last-minute reproduction of the papers. Eugene Stanley, Richmond Thomason, and Lindsay Childs, all Wesleyan undergraduates, made themselves highly useful in a variety of ways; Kenneth Wing, also a student, capably managed the tape recorder for many hours. Louis Mink, who declines to be regarded as a member of the committee for the conference, deserves the gratitude of all of the participants for having arranged for the use of the Faculty Club and for performing numerous other chores. Mrs. Henry E. Kyburg, Jr., contributed her time and energy as receptionist and errand girl. We are grateful to Robert Rosenbaum, to whose original inspiration we owe the idea of having such a conference, and to Sigmund Neumann, who gave us the benefit of his experience and support. Our greatest debt, however, is to Paul Shiman, who not only took a large part in organizing the conference from the beginning, but whose energy, enthusiasm, and unflagging attention to detail were instrumental in allowing the conference to run smoothly. He cheerfully took on chore after unpleasant chore, and performed them all well. Finally, we must thank all of the participants of the conference for the high level at which they maintained the discussion and for the enthusiasm with which they took part. Nearly every one ended up with some chore or other to perform, and we are delighted that these chores were all performed so well.

H.E.K., Jr.

Introduction

By Ernest Nagel

Although the study of inductive reasoning and probable inference is often supposed to be of concern primarily to professional philosophers, this opinion is belied by the numerous fundamental contributions to the long history of the subject that have been made by mathematicians, and by natural and social scientists, as well as by philosophers. Moreover, many facets of the subject are being vigorously explored today by students who are associated with an even wider assortment of specialized disciplines than in the past. Indeed, in view of the conspicuous place inductive reasoning occupies in all adaptive behavior and in all inquiries into matters of fact, as well as in view of the increasingly prominent role that probabilistic notions have come to play in both the theoretical and the applied sciences, it would be surprising if active interest in questions concerning induction were limited to members of a single profession. But in any case, in consequence of the great variety of current investigations into diverse aspects of the subject, even an account of only the more salient of these studies cannot easily avoid discussing some questions whose bearing on other matters also examined may be far from clear. Accordingly, although the papers in the present volume were prepared for a conference on current problems of induction and are therefore addressed to phases of a common subject matter, just how they are related to one another is not uniformly obvious and is in some cases admittedly problematic.

The relevance of the essays to one another can be properly assessed only if the specific problems with which they deal are placed within the inclusive but distinct contexts in which the problems are generated. This cannot be done adequately in brief compass. But a useful perspective on these contexts can perhaps be gained by classifying the numerous questions about induction under a few major categories, subsuming under them the specific problems discussed in this volume, and noting some of the still unresolved or controversial issues associated with several of these categories. This Introduction is an attempt to provide such a perspective.

The extensive literature on induction and probability can be grouped under the following three main heads: (1) empirical studies of inductive behavior; (2) formal theories and calculi of non-demonstrative inference; and (3) discussions bearing on the interpretation, application and validation of probability statements. Each of these labels covers a distinctive type of inquiry; but as will soon be apparent, investigations belonging to one type frequently take for granted some of the results obtained in inquiries of another type.

I

Since discussions of induction are in general not addressed to a purely speculative notion without application to any existing subject matter, they are inevitably carried on within some framework of assumptions about the ways in which men acquire and distinguish beliefs that have some measure of reliability. (Although the communication of beliefs by formal instruction is one of these ways, it will be ignored in what follows.) Moreover, if such assumptions are not to count simply as arbitrary postulates, they are presumably based on observations of relevant features of actual human conduct. Accordingly, the empirical study of human behavior directed to securing more or less reliable beliefs appears to be the ultimate point of departure for all discussions of induction.

In any event, the question as to how knowledge is actually acquired has been of perennial interest since classical antiquity. Among the forms assumed by the many efforts to illuminate this question are the following: generalized descriptions of stages in the development of intellectual maturity in human beings; discussions of personal habits and environmental circumstances that have allegedly been favorable to successful inquiry; systematic experimental studies of biological and psychological mechanisms that are operative in processes of learning and adaptation (Dr. Berlyne's paper in this volume surveys some recent work of this type); biographical accounts, based in part on the scientific publications and other relevant writings of individual scientists, which present in sequential order the steps they took in arriving at their discoveries; proposals of theoretical models, often suggested by ideas fruitfully employed at the time in some other branch of science, to explain the cognitive capacities of the human organism (an approach illustrated in this volume by Dr. Ashby's paper); analyses of the influence of social and intellectual factors during various historical periods upon the growth of scientific and other knowledge; codifications of standards actually used, whether or not explicitly professed, in judging the acceptability of claims to knowledge in different disciplines at different times; and investigations of the historical careers of various claims to knowledge, with a view to assessing the effective merits of different standards that have been employed in judging the worth of those claims.

No one will seriously maintain that these far-flung investigations completely answer the question of how knowledge is acquired, but there is also no doubt that they have contributed much toward resolving it. Moreover, some of them are clearly pertinent to discussions of induction belonging to the other types mentioned above. For example, empirical study shows that beliefs about matters of fact are generally accepted on evidence which lacks demonstrative force, that the frequency of successful action undertaken in the light of such beliefs varies with the character and composition of the evidence for them, and that there is therefore a patent need for analyzing systematically and correcting when necessary the unexpressed habits as well as the explicitly formulated rules employed in non-demonstrative reasoning. On the other hand, these investigations appear to lend no support to the claim, repeatedly made in the past and revived by some recent writers, that advances in scientific knowledge have been consequent to the use of a so-called "logic of discovery," consisting of definite rules which codify effective ways for acquiring new ideas or gaining fresh knowledge. However, perhaps the largest part of the material falling into this category is concerned with the causal conditions (biological, psychological, or social) for the occurrence of various traits of inductive behavior. In consequence, most of the investigations in this category are undoubtedly irrelevant to the formal and normative issues discussed in the other two divisions of the entire subject of induction (as Dr. Kessen clearly notes in his comments in this volume on Dr. Berlyne's paper).

II

The central concern of the second group of studies on induction is to codify and explore systematically the formal principles of non-demonstrative reasoning. This task was begun by mathematicians of the

seventeenth century, who introduced most of the key ideas for a quantitative calculus of probability; and while logicians, physicists, and
statisticians subsequently also made important contributions to the
axiomatization of probability theory or its technical development, the
task has remained to a large extent a special province for mathematical
research. Indeed, although the calculus of probability was initially constructed with an eye to certain applications, it eventually became evident
that the purely mathematical content of the calculus can be presented
with no particular interpretation in mind—for example, by expounding
it, as is often done currently, in terms of the notions of abstract set and
measure theory. In consequence, a large fraction of the literature on the
calculus of probability and its ramified applications is of technical interest
primarily to specialists in some branch of pure mathematics, mathematical physics, or theoretical statistics.

Nevertheless, to obtain an orientation in this domain of formal
analysis, it will be helpful to recall briefly the three major conceptions of
probability that continue to stimulate work in the field. Perhaps the oldest
of these, regarded for a time by many students as wholly inadequate but
currently undergoing a vigorous renascence, is the view that probability
judgments simply state the degree of subjective or personal conviction
with which beliefs are held on the basis of given evidence, and that a
calculus of probability is just a set of plausible rules for making mutually
consistent such degrees of belief. According to the second conception,
probability is a logical relation between evidential statements and the
hypothesis supported by them, the relation possessing degrees corresponding to the strength of such support and coinciding in the limiting
case with the relation of logical entailment. Although most proponents
of the two conceptions of probability thus far mentioned maintain that
degrees of probability can always be assigned quantitative measures, there
are others who deny that this is always possible. The third conception is
the notion that probability is the relative frequency in "the long run" (or
in the limit) with which some designated trait occurs in a given set of
elements (or reference class), so that in this view degrees of probability
are invariably associated with a numerical measure.

In elaborating these conceptions, their advocates have been compelled
to face a large number of essentially formal problems, which can be
classified under a few types. In the first place, there is the question of
whether any of these notions of probability is *explicitly* definable in terms

of more basic and perhaps clearer ideas, and if so in what manner. Although the possibility of such definitions for the first two notions is denied by some of their proponents, much effort has been devoted in connection with all three conceptions to showing in detail not only how this may be done but also how numerical measures for degrees of probability might be assigned. Second, irrespective of the position taken on the definability of "probability," a great deal of labor has gone into formulating suitable axioms, with a view to obtaining a calculus consonant either with some particular interpretation of probability or even with several interpretations that often seem *prima facie* mutually incompatible. (An axiomatization of this latter sort is presented by Dr. Leblanc's paper in this volume.) An obvious phase of this type of formal analysis is the discovery of new theorems that are implied by a given set of axioms, with the consequent enlargement of the known range of specific problems with which the calculus can deal. In the third place, by introducing additional postulates concerning the probable outcomes of various alternative courses of action as well as concerning the "utilities" that may be associated with such outcomes, theoretical statistics has developed probability theory in the direction of constructing criteria for judging estimates of unknown parameters or for testing statistical hypotheses in the light of evidence obtained from random samplings of a population. (The contributions of Drs. Robbins and Braithwaite belong in part to this type of analysis.) Fourth and finally, there is the question of incorporating one or another of these notions of probability into various substantive theories of empirical science (such as physics, biology, or the study of human behavior). However, since work of this type requires not only competence in handling formal problems of mathematical probability but also expert familiarity with concrete factual issues, it is usually regarded as falling into the province of some special branch of science.

III

The third category of studies on induction contains what is undoubtedly the most controversial literature of the subject, and is commonly regarded as its distinctively "philosophical" branch. It is perhaps most usefully characterized in terms of a number of major problems.

A. It is generally assumed that two important tasks of science are to provide explanations and to make predictions. Accordingly, since principles of inductive inference must be employed in evaluating whether these tasks are successfully achieved, students of induction are confronted with the problem of distinguishing and analyzing types of scientific explanation and prediction, even if this task is subordinate to their main concern. (The papers in this volume by Drs. Grünbaum, Hanson, and Morgenbesser deal with aspects of this problem, and examine the much discussed issues of whether there is an inherent difference between explanation and prediction, what the formal requirements for satisfactory explanations are, and in particular whether every satisfactory scientific explanation makes explicit or tacit use of either strictly universal or statistical laws.)

B. Although it is certainly possible to distinguish sharply between formal problems within some proposed calculus of inductive inference (i.e., problems that are "logical" in the narrow sense of the word) and methodological questions involved in interpreting and applying the calculus, it is also clear that, insofar as such a calculus is presumed to codify rules of evaluating evidence, it is not possible to assess its merits without reference to methodological considerations. Several issues of paramount importance in this connection are subjects of current debate.

1. Serious doubts have been expressed as to whether it is possible to construct calculi which will systematize principles of inductive inference. Indeed, some of these doubts extend to denying that there are in fact any generally accepted and unquestionably valid principles for assessing evidence—an extreme view that is difficult to reconcile with what is known about the actual conduct of inquiry. On the other hand, other thinkers are simply skeptical about the feasibility of assigning quantitative measures to the strength of evidence. The fact that no satisfactory system of such measures has been devised, despite the repeated efforts to do so, gives point to this skepticism. However, the possibility of constructing such a system cannot be dismissed as inherently absurd, even if to many students success may seem unlikely. Only the future can decide whether the possibility will ever be realized.

2. There is nevertheless considerable agreement that the rules of inductive inference can be codified systematically, and that up to a point most if not all the existing calculi of probability yield *some* principles for assessing the weight of evidence that are *prima facie* sound. On the other

hand, there is no general consensus as to what is a satisfactory interpretation for an adequate calculus or whether *all* the principles entailed by any of the extant calculi are really sound. The following are a few examples of such moot issues.

Many rules frequently proposed for assessing evidence are based on the assumption that the evidential support for a given hypothesis can be evaluated without reference to alternative hypotheses. However, this assumption is in disagreement with what is usually acknowledged to be sound scientific practice, and appears to correspond to the limiting case in which there happens to be no serious alternatives to the hypothesis under consideration. (The papers of both Drs. Braithwaite and Robbins implicitly reject this assumption.)

Furthermore, several comprehensive systems of inductive logic are in the process of development according to which the probability of a hypothesis is increased by increasing the sheer number of its confirming instances, even if the instances are assumed to be alike in all (or in all relevant) respects. Some thinkers maintain, moreover, that all inductive inference is based ultimately on estimates of the limits of relative frequencies (i.e., on what is traditionally known as "enumerative induction"), and that in a state of so-called "primitive knowledge" (i.e., a state in which we are presumed to have no knowledge at our disposal other than that of past relative frequencies) such estimates can generally be improved by the "self-corrective" procedure of increasing the sheer number of examined instances of a hypothesis. (Dr. Salmon's paper in this volume is a defense of one version of an "inductive rule" implicit in this last claim.) However, to other students of the subject the various rules based on enumerative induction appear to be not only contrary to established scientific practice, but also to be unreasonable when they are analyzed in detail.

Finally, various rules have been proposed in current statistical theory for deciding between alternative statistical hypotheses, where the rules are functions not only of the available evidence for those hypotheses, but also of the assumed "utilities" (i.e., the satisfactions and dissatisfactions) associated with the outcomes of the specific actions that would follow upon the acceptance of a hypothesis. (Dr. Robbins employs this notion in his paper.) These rules have been found to be both illuminating theoretically and of great practical value in applications of statistical theory. Some thinkers (e.g., Dr. Braithwaite) have therefore been stimulated to develop a general theory of inductive inference by enlarging the scope of such statistical decision rules so as to include the case in which alternative hypotheses appear to have only a theoretical import (as in theoretical physics or biology) but have no specific practical consequences. However, without disputing the importance of current statistical decision theory, other students do dispute the cogency of extending the scope of its decision rules to situations for which the supposition that alternative hypotheses are associated with differential utilities seems to be without genuine significance.

C. As is well known, a feature of sound inductive arguments that distinguishes them sharply from valid deductive ones is that in the former the truth of the premises is not necessarily transmitted to their conclusions —that is, even if the evidential premises for a hypothesis in an inductive argument are true, the hypothesis may nevertheless be false. In consequence, students of the subject have been faced with the difficult and still unsettled problem of "justifying" induction: the problem of finding cogent reasons for believing that the generally accepted inductive rules for assessing evidence are indeed sound, not just arbitrary stipulations. None of the papers in this volume deals with this problem explicitly, though Dr. Salmon's essay as well as the comments of some of its discussants do so indirectly; and it may therefore be useful to canvass briefly the major positions on this central question that continue to receive serious attention. Ignoring those who profess a radical skepticism concerning all inductive arguments, as well as those who regard the problem of justifying inductive principles as hopelessly insoluble but nevertheless accept them as matters of "animal faith," five such positions can be distinguished.

1. Perhaps the best-known way of attempting to resolve the problem is to introduce some global material assumption about the constitution of the universe (e.g., the familiar "principle of the uniformity of nature" of J. S. Mill or some modern variants of this principle), on the strength of which inductive arguments are then claimed to be justified deductively. However, quite apart from the question as to whether the alleged deductions from the assumption are valid or even whether it makes good sense to suppose that inductive arguments can be transformed into deductive ones, since the assumption is a factual one and must be known either to be true or to have a non-zero degree of probability, this approach to the problem appears to resolve it only by generating an issue that is identical with the one it claims to settle.

2. Many thinkers have therefore concluded that the justification of induction cannot rest upon any empirical premises, whether comprehensively universal or narrowly particular. According to some who subscribe to this view, moreoever, the entire edifice of inductive logic must be based upon a small number of ultimate principles of inductive inference each of which can be recognized as inherently "rational" and self-evidently true, although none of them is true simply in virtue of the meanings of its constituent terms. For example, allegedly one such principle is that the probability of a hypothesis on given evidence is not altered under permutations of the individual constants (or proper names) contained in those statements. It is not clear, however, why even a supposedly self-evident principle for assessing evidence should be accepted as rational, unless the assessments are found to be generally reliable—that is, unless the conclusions of arguments judged to be sound in the light of the principle turn out to be in agreement with the empirical facts in a sufficiently large proportion of cases. On the other hand, if the inherent rationality claimed for a principle of induction is assumed to guarantee its reliability in this sense, the proposed justification of induction appears to be a revival of classical aprioristic rationalism and to be confronted with the familiar difficulties of that philosophy.

3. There is, however, another approach adopted by some students who seek to justify induction without employing any empirical assumptions According to them, the aim of all science can be reduced to the task of ascertaining the limits of the relative frequencies with which various types of events occur—even though, as they also claim, we can have no assurance that such limits exist or know with certainty the actual values of these limits if indeed they do exist. Nevertheless, so it is argued, *if* such a limit does exist for a given event, it is analytically true (as a consequence of the definition of the term "limit") that we are eventually bound to obtain a close approximation of its value by adhering to the following inductive rule: Take the relative frequency with which the event has been observed to occur as an estimate of the limit, and continue to "correct" this estimate as the number of such observations increases. (It is this "tautological" justification of induction that is at stake in Dr. Salmon's paper and in Dr. Black's comments on it.) But as has already been noted, it is at least debatable whether the principles for assessing evidence can all be reduced to the rule of enumerative induction. Moreoever, even if this question is waived, it is not clear to many students just how the proposed justification

constitutes a rational ground for believing that an estimate of a limit formed on the basis of any number of observations in accordance with the indicated rule, however large this number may be, is even roughly close to the actual value of the limit.

4. Nevertheless, though the view may seem plausible that if induction is to be justified it must be done without employing material premises, a number of thinkers have not found it credible, despite the well-known difficulties in the contrary view. Following some pregnant but undeveloped suggestions of Charles S. Peirce, they believe that rules of induction formulate policies for evaluating evidence, and that like other policies those rules can be judged in the light of their successes in achieving the objectives for which they have been instituted—that is, in terms of their practical worth as instruments for securing reliable knowledge. Accordingly, these students have tried to show that the record of successful uses of inductive principles in the past can serve as evidence, but without circularity in the agrument, for the continued success of such principles in the future—in short, that inductive principles can be justified inductively. However, this approach to the problem of justification has not as yet been developed systematically, nor has it fully ironed out some admitted difficulties; and despite its promise, it does not at present enjoy a large following.

5. Finally, many students dismiss the problem of justifying induction as spurious, and as at best a concern over the meaning of the word "rational." They note that while it makes sense to inquire whether some particular action is legal (i.e., in accordance with a given legal system), it is absurd to ask whether the legal system itself is legal. Similarly, they argue that it makes sense to ask whether a belief about some particular matter of fact is justified, since the question involves asking whether there are rational grounds for accepting the belief (i.e., whether the evidence for it is in accordance with inductive principles); and they therefore conclude that to inquire whether inductive principles are themselves justifiable is to pursue the senseless question of whether the grounds for accepting inductive principles are in accordance with inductive principles. This proposed dissolution of the problem has not been found generally convincing, for the analogy between the question as to whether a legal system is legal and the question as to whether inductive principles can be justified has not impressed most students as sound. In any event, the problem continues to engage the attention of many thinkers since

it does not seem at all senseless to them to ask why they should have a rational confidence in the belief that certain rules for assessing evidence are reliable tools for achieving competent knowledge and successful action.

This Introduction does not pretend to give an exhaustive survey of current problems of induction, it advances no solutions for any of them, and it offers no evaluations of solutions proposed by contributors to this volume. Its aim, as has already been mentioned, is to place the technical papers in this volume in a broader framework of ideas than any one of them can properly supply, in order to indicate how these detailed analyses are related to one another and to a large field of inquiry; and this Introduction would take unfair advantage of the authors of those papers (none of whom has had the opportunity to read it), as well as defeat its own aim, if it attempted to pass judgment on their contributions. However, one general evaluative comment may not be inappropriate. The problems of induction are difficult, progress in resolving many of them has been slow and sometimes at a standstill, and it would be absurd to claim that the papers in this volume present indisputably correct solutions to any of them. There are nevertheless no compelling reasons for believing that the difficulties attendant to those problems are insuperable; and this volume provides added grounds for confidence that those difficulties are not impervious to painstaking analysis, attention to details, and concerted attack.

INDUCTION : Some Current Issues

I

Statistical and Inductive Probabilities

HUGUES LEBLANC

I SHOULD like to address this conference on the topic of statistical and inductive probabilities; review the ways in which statistical probabilities are commonly allotted to sets; show how the probabilities in question may be turned over to the well-formed formulas of a family of languages, the languages L, and thereupon prove to be truth-values or functions of such; review the ways in which inductive probabilities are commonly allotted to the well-formed formulas of the languages L; note that the probabilities in question qualify as estimates of truth-values or functions of such and hence as estimates of statistical probabilities; and finally comment on what I take to be the two outstanding problems in probability theory today.

I

A brief survey of the languages L, that is, the master language L^∞ and its sublanguages L^1, L^2, L^3, and so on, may be in order.

First, the syntax of the languages L. The primitive signs of L^∞ are to be: (1) a denumerably infinite number of individual constants arranged in some alphabetical order; (2) a like number of individual variables also arranged in some alphabetical order; (3) a finite number of predicate constants; (4) the identity sign '='; (5) the two connectives '~' and '⊃'; (6) the quantifier letter 'Ɐ'; and (7) the two parentheses '(' and ')'. For each N from 1 on, the primitive signs of L^N are to be the first N individual constants under (1) plus all the signs under (2)–(7). The notions of a well-formed formula (hereafter wff) of L, a free occurrence in a wff of L of an individual variable of L, a sentence (or, if so preferred, a closed wff) of L, a quasi-sentence (or, if so preferred, an open wff) of L, and a state-description of L^N are carried over unchanged from the literature. A quantifier-and-identity-free sentence of L is to be a sentence of L which contains no occurrence of 'Ɐ' and '='. An instance in L of a wff of L is to be the wff itself if the wff happens to be a sentence, any result of substituting individual constants of L for all the free occurrences in the wff of individual variables of L if the wff happens to be a quasi-sentence. Finally, various familiar signs (the connectives 'v', '&', and '≡', the quantifier letter 'Ǝ', signs from the theory of virtual sets, and so on) are presumed to be grafted to the languages L by means of suitable definitions.

Second, the semantics of the languages L. Individuals, to be collectively referred to as $U_{L\infty}$, are presumed to be assigned to the individual constants of L^∞ as the individuals designated in L^∞ by those constants, different individuals being assigned to different constants; a set of n–tuples consisting of n (not necessarily distinct) members of $U_{L\infty}$ is presumed to be assigned to each n–place predicate constant of L^∞ as the extension in L^∞ of that constant; the individuals, to be collectively referred to as U_{LN}, which are designated in L^∞ by the individual constants of L^N (and hence of L^∞) are presumed to be designated in L^N by the said constants; and the set of all the n–tuples which belong to the extension in L^∞ of each n–place predicate constant of L^N (and hence of L^∞) and consist of members of U_{LN} is presumed to be the extension in L^N of the said constant. A sentence of L is said to be true in L under the same conditions as in Carnap,[1] (sentences of the form (ⱯW)A, for example, being true in L if all the instances of A in L are true in L), a sentence of L is to be false in L if it is not true in L, and the truth–value in L (Tv, for short) of a sentence of L is to be 1 or 0 depending upon whether the sentence is true in L or false in L. A wff of L is to be valid in L (or, if so preferred, a theorem of L) under the standard conditions to be found in the literature and the following additional two: any wff of the form $\sim (W = X)$ is to be valid in L if W and X are two different individual constants of L, and any wff of L^N of the form $A_1 \supset (A_2 \supset (\dots (A_N \supset (ⱯW)A) \dots))$ is to be valid in L^N if, for each i from 1 to N, A_i is the result of substituting the i-th individual constant of L^N for all the free occurrences of W in A.[2] Finally, a sentence of L is to be logically true in L if it is valid in L, to be logically

[1] *Logical Foundations of Probability*, Berkeley, University of California Press, 1950; sec. 17. The languages L come from this work.

[2] It follows from the second of those two conditions that if every instance in L^N of a quasi-sentence A of L^N is valid in L^N, then (ⱯW) A is valid in L^N. The analogous result for L^∞ is provable without benefit of any additional condition, as Professor Stig Kanger pointed out to me.

false in L if its negation is valid in L, to logically imply in L another sentence of L if the conditional formed out of the first sentence as antecedent and the second as consequent is valid in L, and to be logically equivalent in L to another sentence of L if the biconditional formed out of the two sentences is valid in L.

II

The various subsets of a finite set U, a set dubbed for the occasion *a probability set*, are normally allotted probabilities in either one of two ways. According to the first procedure, real numbers, called *elementary probabilities*, or *measures*, or (as I shall have it here) *weights*, are first allotted to the various members of U, the numbers in question being subject to two restrictions: (a1) each one of them must be non-negative; and (a2) their sum must be equal to 1. A number, called *an absolute probability* or, for short, *a probability*, is then allotted to each subset of U, the number in question being the sum of the weights of the members of U which belong to the said subset. According to the second procedure, real numbers, called *probabilities*, are directly allotted to the various subsets of U, the numbers in question being subject to three restrictions: (b1) each one of them must be non-negative; (b2) the number allotted to U must be 1; and (b3) the number allotted to the union of two non-overlapping subsets must be equal to the sum of the numbers allotted to the two subsets. To round out the picture, a number, called *a weight*, may then be allotted to each member of U, the number in question being the probability of the unit set of the said member of U. The two procedures clearly yield the same allotments of weights and probabilities.

Sets of n-tuples of members of a finite probability set U boast probabilities, too. (1) By an obvious extension of the first procedure I just described, real numbers, called *weights*, are sometimes allotted to the various n-tuples of members of U, the numbers in question being subject again to restrictions (a1)–(a2) above, and a number, called *a probability*, allotted to each set of n-tuples of members of U, the number in question being the sum of the weights of the n-tuples which belong to the said set. (2) Sometimes also the weight of an n-tuple of members of U is taken to be the product of the weights of the members of U which make up the n-tuple and the probability of a set of n-tuples of members of U then calculated as in (1). Procedure (2), though commonly resorted to only when the members of U are deemed stochastically independent, is simpler than procedure (1). I shall accordingly favor it here for expository purposes.[3]

The various pairs of subsets of a finite probability set U are normally allotted probabilities as follows. Let the members of U be allotted weights; let the subsets of U be allotted (absolute) probabilities; and let two subsets of U, the second one of which is presumed to be allotted a non-zero (absolute) probability, be given. The *conditional probability* or, for short, *probability* of the first subset given the second, and hence of the pair of subsets, is then taken to be the ratio of the (absolute) probability of the intersection of the two subsets to the (absolute) probability of the second.

Subsets and pairs of subsets of a denumerably infinite probability set U may be allotted probabilities by variants of the above procedures or by a limit procedure, the latter procedure permissible of course only when U is serially ordered.

The probabilities considered so far are what Carnap and others have called *statistical probabilities*. Though originally intended for sets, they may be turned over to such wffs as the wffs of L, as I pointed out in my 1959 paper and Kemeny and his collaborators likewise pointed out in their *Finite Mathematical Structures* of the same year.[4]

Consider first a sentence A of L. It can readily be shown that either $\hat{W}A = U$ or $\hat{W}A = \cap$ is true in L depending upon whether A is true in L or A is false in L.[5] I accordingly suggest that the statistical probability $Ps(A)$ of A in L be taken to be 1 (the probability which would normally be allotted to U) when A is true in L, 0 (the probability which would normally be allotted to $\cap$) when A is false in L. Consider next a quasi-sentence A of L which contains free occurrences of a single individual variable of L, say W. It can readily be shown that $W' \in \hat{W}A$ is true in L^N if and only if A' is true in L^N, where W' is an individual constant of L^N and A' is the result of substituting W' for all the free occurrences of W in A. I accordingly suggest that the weights which would normally be allotted to the members of U be passed on to the individual constants

---

[3] Following the advice of R. Jeffrey, I have made procedure (1) my official procedure in the monograph of footnote 14.

[4] See J. G. Kemeny, H. Mirkil, J. L. Snell, and G. L. Thompson, *Finite Mathematical Structures*, New York, Prentice-Hall, 1959, pp. 60–70 and 112–16.

[5] U, the so-called universal set, is identical of course with U_{L^∞} in L^∞, with U_{L^N} in L^N.

of L^N and that the statistical probability $Ps^N(A)$ of A in L^N be taken to be the sum

$$\sum_{i=1}^{N} (w^N(W_i) \times Ps^N(A_i)),$$

where, for each i from 1 to N, W_i is the i-th individual constant of L^N, $w^N(W_i)$ is the weight of W_i in L^N, A_i is the result of substituting W_i for all the free occurrences of W in A, and $Ps^N(A_i)$ is the statistical probability of A_i in L^N. I also suggest that the statistical probability $Ps^\infty(A)$ of A in L^∞ be taken to be the limit if any for increasing N of the sum

$$\sum_{i=1}^{N} (w^N(W_i) \times Ps^\infty(A_i)),$$

where, for each i from 1 to N, W_i is the i-th individual constant of L^∞ and hence of L^N, $w^N(W_i)$ is the weight of W_i in L^N, A_i is the result of substituting W_i for all the free occurrences of W in A, and $Ps^\infty(A_i)$ is the statistical probability of A_i in L^∞. Consider next a quasi-sentence A of L which contains free occurrences of $n + 1$ individual variables of L. I suggest that the statistical probability $Ps(A)$ of A in L be taken to be the sum or the limit I just described, but with the last one of the $n + 1$ variables in question doing duty throughout the description for W.[6] Consider finally a pair of wffs A and B of L, a pair such that the two statistical probabilities $Ps(A \& B)$ and $Ps(B)$ exist. I suggest that the statistical probability $Ps(A, B)$ of A given B in L be taken to be the ratio $Ps(A \& B)/Ps(B)$ when $Ps(B)$ is non-zero, the number 1 when $Ps(B)$ is zero.

Identical suggestions will be found in my 1959 paper with $w^N(W_i)$

---

[6] It follows from the suggestion in the text that $Ps^N(A)$, where, for example, A is a quasi-sentence of L^N containing free occurrences of two individual variables of L^N, say W and W', is equal to the double sum

$$\sum_{i=1}^{N} \sum_{j=1}^{N} (w^N(W_i, W'_j) \times Ps^N(A_{i,j})),$$

where, for each i and 1 to N and each j from 1 to N, W_i and W'_j are the i-th and j-th individual constants of L^N, $w^N(W_i, W'_j)$ is the product of the weights in L^N of W_i and W'_j, $A_{i,j}$ is the result of substituting W_i for all the free occurrences of W in A and W'_j for all the free occurrences of W' in A, and $Ps^N(A_{i,j})$ is the statistical probability of $A_{i,j}$ in L^N. Following the advice of R. Jeffrey, I have modified the definition of $Ps(A)$ in the monograph of footnote 14 so as to conform with procedure (1) of page 5. The same remark applies to my definition of $P_i(A)$ below.

presumed for the occasion to equal $1/N$. Roughly similar suggestions will also be found in *Finite Mathematical Structures*. Kemeny and his collaborators restrict themselves, however, to quasi-sentences hailing from a finite language and containing free occurrences of a single individual variable; they also allot other probabilities besides 1 and 0 to sentences, a matter I have criticized elsewhere.[7]

It can be shown that $Ps(A)$, as I define it, meets the wff-theoretic analogues of restrictions (b1)–(b3) above (on page 5) and that $Ps(A, B)$, again as I define it, meets the wff-theoretic analogues of restrictions commonly imposed upon conditional probabilities. It can likewise be shown that $Ps(A)$ is the truth-value of A in L when A is a sentence of L, a weighted sum of the truth-values in L^N of the various instances of A in L^N when A is a quasi-sentence of L^N containing free occurrences of a single individual variable of L^N, the limit if any for increasing N of a weighted sum of the truth-values in L^∞ of the so-called first N instances of A in L^∞ when A is a quasi-sentence of L^∞ containing free occurrences of a single individual variable of L^∞, and so on. The latter result is readily forthcoming, $Ps(A)$ being equal by definition to $Tv(A)$ when A is a sentence of L. It may nonetheless be of interest, since it brings into the open what so many have so long suspected: that the statistical probabilities normally allotted to sets are nothing but truth-values or functions of truth-values under disguise.

III

I suggested above that the statistical probability in L of a sentence A of L be taken to be 1 when A is true in L, 0 when A is false in L. The statistical probability in L of a sentence A of L given another sentence B of L proves as a consequence to equal 1 when B is false in L or A is true in L, 0 otherwise. Those who would like to gauge by means of statistical probabilities the wisdom of drawing a conclusion A of L from a premise B of L will perhaps wince at the result. It is possible, however, to measure what I call *the coefficient of statistical reliability of an inference* without tampering with the allotment in question.

Suppose we are given: (1) a premise B and a conclusion A, which,

---

[7] See "On a recent allotment of probabilities to open and closed sentences," *Notre Dame Journal of Formal Logic*, vol. 1 (1960), pp. 171–75.

for simplicity's sake, I shall assume to be sentences of a sublanguage L^N of L^∞, contain occurrences of a single individual constant of L^N, the same constant, say W, in each case, and contain no quantifier; (2) the pair of results B' and A' (called later on *the individual-constant-free-associates of B and A*) of substituting the first individual variable of L^N which is foreign to B and A, say X, for all the free occurrences of W in B and A respectively; and (3) the N pairs B_1' and A_1', B_2' and A_2', ... , and B_N' and A_N' of results of substituting the first, the second, ... , and the N-th individual constant of L^N for all the occurrences of X in B' and A' respectively. Suppose next that, instead of merely drawing A from B if B is true in L^N, we go through all the pairs listed in (3) and draw A_1' from B_1' if B_1' is true in L^N, A_2' from B_2' if B_2' is true in L^N, ... , and A_N' from B_N' if B_N' is true in L^N. Suppose next that, as each conclusion is drawn, we chalk one up for ourselves when the conclusion turns out to be true in L^N. Suppose finally that, the last conclusion drawn, we add up the ones (if any) we chalked up for ourselves and divide the resulting sum by the number of conclusions drawn in the process. Assuming, as I do here for simplicity's sake, that each individual constant of L^N is allotted $1/N$ as its weight in L^N, we might well treat the resulting figure as the coefficient of statistical reliability, CRs(A, B) for short, of the inference leading from B to A. But CRs(A, B) is easily shown to equal Ps(A', B'). I accordingly conclude that the wisdom of drawing a conclusion A of L from a premise B of L, where A and B are two sentences of the kind under discussion, can be gauged by means of statistical probabilities in spite of the 1 or 0 which Ps is bound to take as its value for any pair of sentences of L.

The same result holds for other pairs of sentences A and B of L. The definition of CRs(A, B) calls, however, in such cases for a number of adjustments which proponents of gauges like CRs(A, B) (Peirce, Williams, Ajdukiewicz, and so on) may have ignored. I unfortunately cannot list them here.

One outstanding matter remains to be discussed before I turn to so-called *inductive probabilities*, the selection of the weights to be allotted in a set-theoretic context to the members of a finite probability set U, in a wff-theoretic context to the individual constants of a sublanguage L^N of L^∞. The matter is often cavalierly dismissed, not only in primers of probability theory, but in advanced treatises as well.

Study of the literature would indicate that unequal weights are allotted to the members of a finite probability set U in two major kinds of cases. In cases of the first kind we are advised to allot unequal weights to the n members of U because two of those members, for example, may be indistinguishable from each other and each one of them as a result rates only half the weight allotted to each one of the remaining n-2 members of U. To illustrate matters, suppose two coins are tossed in succession and that for some reason or other the two coins cannot be told apart. Considering the experiment as still susceptible to four outcomes, say o_1, o_2, o_3, and o_4, we might allot each one of o_1, o_2, o_3, and o_4 a weight of $1/4$; we might also allot the two undistinguishable outcomes, say o_2 and o_3, only half the weight we would allot outcomes o_1 and o_4. Under the second allotment, namely: $1/3$, $1/6$, $1/6$, $1/3$, the probability of the subset of $\{o_1, o_2, o_3, o_4\}$ which is to consist of the actual outcome or outcomes of the experiment will equal $1/3$ however the experiment may terminate, a circumstance which does militate in favor of the allotment.

I gladly leave it to set-theorists to spell out the conditions under which two members of a probability set U might be said to be indistinguishable in U. I shall quote, however, those under which the individuals designated in L by two individual constants, say W and X, of L may be said to be indistinguishable in L. First, $F(W) \equiv F(X)$ should be true in L for each one-place predicate F of L; second, $(\forall Y) (F(W, Y) \equiv F(X, Y))$ and $(\forall Y) (F(Y, W) \equiv F(Y, X))$ should be true in L for each two-place predicate F of L; and so on.

So much for cases of the first kind. Cases of the second kind raise in my opinion a fundamental difficulty and should as a result be dismissed. Imagine a coin has been tossed 100 times, has landed heads up 41 times, and is about to be tossed 100 more times. I would be willing, on the face of it at any rate, to estimate at .41 the fraction of the times the coin will have landed heads up by the close of the entire experiment and hence, allotting each one of the 200 tosses a weight of $1/200$, to estimate at .41 the statistical probability of the set of those among the actual outcomes of the 200 tosses in which the coin has landed or will land heads up. Many writers, though agreeable, to be sure, to estimating the said probability at the same figure, would go one better, set at .41 the weight of the coin landing heads up if tossed once more on some future occasion, and defend the allotment in question, on the grounds that, if tossed not only once more but again and again on future occasions, the coin could be trusted in view of its past behavior to land heads up 41 per cent of the time.

This legerdemain, whereby an estimate of a probability, the statistical probability of a set of actual outcomes, is made to serve as a weight, the weight of a possible outcome, seems to me quite objectionable. Statistical probabilities and hence weights should not, in my opinion, be advertised on one page as measurements on sets and prove on the next to be predictions of such measurements. True, the measurements on sets we call probabilities may frequently be inaccessible and hence have to be surmised in some fashion or other. But surmises of one measurement, say the statistical probability of a set of actual outcomes, should not be passed off as another measurement, say the weight of a possible outcome.

There may be other grounds besides indistinguishability for discriminating against certain members of a finite probability set or certain individual constants of L^N and hence allotting them lesser weights. The literature, however, is rather mum on the subject.

IV

Pairs of sentences of L have been allotted inductive probabilities by Carnap and others in the following fashion. A function Pi^N with pairs of sentences of L^N as its arguments, with real numbers as its values, and meeting the following six requirements or equivalents thereof:

(a) $0 \leq Pi^N(A, B)$,

(b) $Pi^N(A, A) = 1$,

(c) If A and B are logically equivalent in L^N, then
$Pi^N(A, C) = Pi^N(B, C)$,

(d) If B and C are logically equivalent in L^N, then
$Pi^N(A, B) = Pi^N(A, C)$,

(e) $Pi^N(A \& B, C) = Pi^N(A, B \& C) \times Pi^N(B, C)$,

(f) If B is not logically false in L^N, then $Pi^N(\sim A, B) = 1 - Pi^N(A, B)$,

is first assumed to be on hand for each sublanguage L^N of L^∞.[8] $Pi^\infty(A, B)$, where A and B are two sentences of L^∞, is then taken

---

[8] Requirements (a)–(f) are essentially due to G. H. von Wright, *The Logical Problem of Induction*, 2nd rev. ed., New York, Macmillan, 1957, pp. 92–3. For a study of requirements (a)–(f) and equivalents thereof, see my two papers "On Logically False Evidence Statements," *The Journal of Symbolic Logic*, XXII (1957), pp. 345–49, and "On Requirements for Conditional Probability Functions," *ibidem*, xxv (1960), pp. 238–42. Carnap's account of the whole matter will be found in *Logical Foundations of Probability*, ch. 5.

to be the limit if any for increasing i of $Pi^{N+1}(A, B)$, where L^N is the first sublanguage of L^∞ of which both A and B are sentences.

Enlarging upon indications in my 1959 paper, I suggest that further pairs of wffs of L be allotted inductive probabilities along the following lines. First, when A is a quasi-sentence of L containing free occurrences of a single individual variable of L, say W, and B is a sentence of L, I suggest that the inductive probability $Pi(A, B)$ of A given B in L be taken to be the sum

$$\sum_{i=1}^{N} (w^N(W_i) \times Pi^N(A_i, B))$$

or the limit if any for increasing N of the sum

$$\sum_{i=1}^{N} (w^N(W_i) \times Pi^\infty(A_i, B)),$$

where, for each i from 1 to N, W_i is the i-th individual constant of L^N or of L^∞, $w^N(W_i)$ is the weight of W_i in L^N, A_i is the result of substituting W_i for all the free occurrences of W in A, $Pi^N(A_i, B)$ is the statistical probability of A_i given B in L^N, and $Pi^\infty(A_i, B)$ is the statistical probability of A_i given B in L^∞. Second, when A is a quasi-sentence of L containing free occurrences of $n + 1$ individual variables of L and B is a sentence of L, I suggest that the inductive probability $Pi(A, B)$ of A given B in L be taken to be the sum or the limit I just described, but with the last one of the $n + 1$ variables in question doing duty throughout the description for W.

To dispose of a minor technicality, I shall call *regular* any function which meets the six requirements listed above; I shall next call *weakly regular* any function which meets the first five of those requirements plus the following weak analogue of requirement (f):

(f'). If $Pi^N(B, LT) \neq 0$, where LT is an arbitrary logical truth of L^N, then $Pi^N(\sim A, B) = 1 - Pi^N(A, B)$.

Various interpretations of $Pi(A, B)$ are to be found in the literature. I have proposed in recent papers a partly novel one under which $Pi(A, B)$ constitutes an estimate made in the light of the sentence B of L of the statistical probability $Ps(A)$ in L of the sentence or quasi-sentence A of L.[9]

---

[9] See "On Chances and Estimated Chances of Being True" and, especially, "A New Interpretation of c(h,e)," *Philosophy and Phenomenological Research*, vol. 21 (1961), pp. 373–76. The interpretation stems in part from Carnap's treatment of inductive probabilities as estimates of relative frequencies in *Logical Foundations of Probability*, pp. 168–75 and 540–50.

I should like to defend it here briefly, especially in the critical case where A is a sentence of L^N and $Ps^N(A)$ proves to be the truth-value $Tv^N(A)$ of A in L^N.

A few results concerning the sentences of L^N are first presumed to be familiar: (1) that to each sentence A of L^N there corresponds a quantifier-and-identity-free sentence B of L^N which is logically equivalent in L^N to A; and (2) that every quantifier-and-identity-free sentence B of L^N which is not logically false in L^N is logically equivalent in L^N to a state-description of L^N or to a disjunction of two or more state-descriptions of L^N. In view of (1) and (2) I shall restrict myself to the so-called representative sentences of L^N, that is, one arbitrary logical falsehood of L^N, the various state-descriptions of L^N, and the various disjunctions of two or more state-descriptions of L^N. The representative sentences of L^N are clearly finite in number; so are the various pairs of representative sentences of L^N; and so, finally, are the various pairs of representative sentences A and B of L^N such that B is not logically false in L^N and does not logically imply A or $\sim$ A in L^N.

Now for my brief. (1) I shall first take it that if a function with pairs of representative sentences of L^N as its arguments and real numbers as its values is to be deductively sound as a truth-value estimating function for L^N, its value for any pair of representative sentences A and B of L^N should lie within the interval $[0, 1]$, equal 1 if B logically implies A in L^N, and equal 0 if B is not logically false in L^N and logically implies $\sim$ A in L^N. (2) I shall next rank deductively sound truth-value estimating functions for L^N by means of their average value for the various pairs of representative sentences A and B of L^N such that B is not logically false in L^N and does not logically imply A or $\sim$ A in L^N. (3) It follows from (1) and (2) that deductively sound truth-value estimating functions for L^N run from one extreme, the function Pi' which in the light of whatever representative sentence B of L^N estimates the truth-value of whatever representative sentence A of L^N at 0, to another extreme, the function Pi'' which in the light of whatever representative sentence B of L^N estimates the truth-value of whatever representative sentence A of L^N at 1. (4) It can be shown that both Pi' and Pi'' satisfy the first five of the six requirements (a)–(f) imposed above upon Pi^N, but fail to satisfy (and hence are ruled out by) requirement (f) or the weak analogue (f') of requirement (f). (5) I conclude on the strength of the first result that any function with pairs of representative sentences of L^N as its arguments and real numbers as its values which satisfies requirements (a)–(e) must rate "at least pass" as a truth-value estimating function for L^N and on the strength of the second result that any such function which satisfies requirements (a)–(e) plus either one of requirements (f) and (f′) must rate "at least fair" as a truth-value estimating function for L^N. That Pi′ and Pi″, by the way, both satisfy the multiplication requirement (e) should exonerate that requirement from all the suspicions recently cast upon it in the literature.[10]

With $Pi^N(A, B)$, where A and B are representative sentences of L^N, rating by the above argument "at least fair" as an estimate made in the light of B of the truth-value of A in L^N, it quickly follows that Pi(A, B), where A is any sentence or quasi-sentence and B any sentence of L, rates "at least fair" as an estimate made in the light of B of the statistical probability of A in L and that the ratio Pi(A′ & B′, LT)/Pi(B′, LT), where A′ and B′ are what I called above the individual-constant-free associates of two sentences A and B of L, and LT is an arbitrary logical truth of L, rates "at least fair" as an estimate of the coefficient of statistical reliability CRs(A, B) of the inference leading from B as a premise to A as a conclusion.

Both results seem to me significant. The first one shows that inductive probabilities, being estimates of statistical probabilities, can be brought into line with statistical probabilities, and hence that the bitter controversy which has been raging among probability theorists ever since the publication of von Mises' *Grundlagen der Wahrscheinlichkeitsrechnung* (1919) and Keynes' *A Treatise on Probability* (1921) can be amicably and, I take it, fruitfully settled. As for the second, it must be owned that statisticians have their way of surmising the set-theoretic counterpart of CRs(A, B) and hence CRs(A, B) itself, when the latter figure, as by definition is almost bound to be the case, is unknown. Writers on induction, however, may welcome word that the ratio Pi(A′ & B′, LT)/Pi(B′, LT) rates "at least fair" as an estimate of CRs(A, B) whether Pi be the inductive probability function implicitly favored by most statisticians or any other of the inductive probability functions considered here.

---

[10] I have not been able to ascertain whether or not Pi′ and Pi″ satisfy further requirements besides (a)–(e) which would be consistent with (f) or with (f′). Were the answer in the negative, the argument I offer in the text for interpreting $Pi^N(A, B)$ as an "at least fair" estimate made in the light of a representative sentence B of L^N of the truth-value in L^N of another representative sentence A of L^N would, in my opinion, prove to be quite strong.

v

Though claiming that the functions which satisfy requirements (a)–(e) plus either one of requirements (f) and (f') rate "at least fair," I would hardly claim that they all rate "good," let alone "excellent," as truth-value estimating functions for L^N. The problem that confronts us here is perhaps best approached via another set of functions known as absolute inductive probability functions.

As weights were allotted above to the individual constants of L^N, so weights may be allotted in the present context to the state-descriptions of L^N, the weights in question being presumed to be either positive as with Carnap or merely non-negative as with von Wright and their sum being presumed to equal 1.[11] The absolute inductive probability $Pi_0^N(A)$ in L^N of a representative sentence A of L^N may then be taken to be 0 if A is logically false in L^N, the weight of A in L^N if A is a state-description of L^N, and the sum of the weights in L^N of the various state-descriptions of L^N which occur in A if A is the disjunction of two or more state-descriptions of L^N. The conditional inductive probability $Pi^N(A, B)$ in L^N of a pair of representative sentences A and B of L^N may finally be taken to be the ratio $Pi_0^N(A \& B)/Pi_0^N(B)$ when $Pi_0^N(B)$ is non-zero, the number 1 when $Pi_0^N(B)$ is zero. It is easily shown that the function Pi^N just defined is regular when the weights in L^N of the state-descriptions of L^N are presumed to be positive, weakly regular when the weights in question are presumed to be merely non-negative.

Carnap published some ten years ago a study of the continuum of ways in which weights may be allotted to the state-descriptions of L^N.[12] The study has not received, in my opinion, the attention it deserves. I shall, however, venture only one comment on it here. Carnap restricts himself to so-called symmetrical allotments, that is, to allotments under which $Pi_0^N(A)$ equals $Pi_0^N(A')$, where, W and W' being two individual constants of L^N, A' is the result of substituting W' for all the occurrences (if any) of W in A and W for all the occurrences (if any) of W' in A. I, for one, should prefer that the weights allotted to the state-descriptions

---

[11] See G. H. von Wright, "Carnap's Theory of Probability," *The Philosophical Review*, vol. 60 (1951), pp. 362–74.

[12] See *The Continuum of Inductive Methods*, University of Chicago Press, 1952; also *Logical Foundations of Probability*, ch. 8.

of L^N depend upon those already allotted to the individual constants of L^N and hence be such that

$$\mathrm{Pi}_0^N(F(W)) - \mathrm{Pi}_0^N(F(W')),$$

$$\mathrm{Pi}_0^N(F(W, X)) - \mathrm{Pi}_0^N(F(W', X)),\ \mathrm{Pi}_0^N(F(X, W)) - \mathrm{Pi}_0^N(F(X, W')),$$

and so on, where in the last two cases X is an individual constant of L^N other than W and W', is smaller than, equal to, or larger than o according as the weight $w^N(W)$ of W in L^N is smaller than, equal to, or larger than the weight $w^N(W')$ of W' in L^N [13] Carnap of course would allot equal weights to the individual constants of L^N and hence feel his partiality for symmetrical allotments justified. However, in the absence of any consensus among set-theorists as to how weights should be allotted to the members of a finite probability set and hence of any consensus as to how weights should be allotted to the individual constants of L^N, I should welcome a somewhat broader study than Carnap's.

My failure to commit myself here to a specific allotment of weights to the state-descriptions of L^N may come as a disappointment. It should not, however, be deemed more shocking than the common failure of set-theorists to allot specific weights to the members of their finite probability sets. How to weight the individual constants of L^N (or, if you prefer, the members of a finite probability set) and how to weight the state-descriptions of L^N seem indeed to me two problems of equal importance and two problems to which probability theorists should address themselves with an equal sense of urgency. As for myself, I shall deem my effort here worthwhile if I have gone some way toward reconciling statistical and inductive probabilities and clearing the way for the ventual solution of those two problems.[14]

[13] Use of $\mathrm{Pi}_0^N(A) - \mathrm{Pi}_0^N(A')$ in place of such subcases of $\mathrm{Pi}_0^N(A) - \mathrm{Pi}_0^N(A')$ as I list in the text would lead to contradiction, as Professor Isador Sheffler has pointed out to me

[14] An early draft of this paper was read at the Pennsylvania State University in April, 1961. The results reported here are part of a monograph, *Statistical and Inductive Probabilities*, Englewood Cliffs, N.J., Prentice-Hall, 1962.

Opening Statement

by Leblanc

T HE objective of the paper is twofold: first, to show that statistical probabilities, once turned over to the sentences of Carnap's languages L, are truth-values or functions of such; and second, to show that inductive probabilities qualify as estimates of truth-values or functions of such and, hence, as estimates of statistical probabilities.

The statistical probability in L of a sentence A of L, $Ps(A)$, for short, is defined as follows:

(a1) If A is a closed sentence of L, then $Ps(A)$ is to be 1 if A is true in L, 0 if A is false in L,

(a2) If A is an open sentence of L^N, then $Ps^N(A)$ is to be

$$\sum_{i=1}^{N} (w^N(W_i) \times Ps^N(A_i)),$$

where W_i is the i-th individual constant of L^N, $w^N(W_i)$ is the weight in L^N of W_i, and A_i is like A except for containing occurrences of W_i wherever A contains free occurrences of some individual variable of L^N,

(a3) If A is an open sentence of L^∞, then $Ps^\infty(A)$ is to be

$$\text{Limit}_{N \to \infty} \sum_{i=1}^{N} (w^N(W_i) \times Ps^\infty(A_i)),$$

where W_i, $w^N(W_i)$, and A_i are as in (a2).

Since $Ps(A)$, where A is a closed sentence of L, equals $Tv(A)$, the truth-value of A in L, it readily follows that the statistical probability in L of a sentence A of L, be A closed or open, is a truth-value or a function of truth-values. When, in particular, $w^N(W_i)$ is set at $1/N$, the statistical probability in L of a sentence A of L proves to be the average truth-value in L of the various instances of A in L.

The inductive probability in L of a sentence A of L given a closed sentence B of L, $Pi(A, B)$ for short, is defined as follows:

(b1) If A is a closed sentence of L^N, then $Pi^N(A, B)$ is to be the value of any function Pi^N (from pairs of closed sentences of L^N to real numbers) which meets six stated requirements,

(b2) If A is a closed sentence of L^∞, then $Pi^\infty(A, B)$ is to be

$$\text{Limit}_{i \to \infty} Pi^{N+i}(A, B),$$

where L^N is the first sublanguage of L^∞ of which both A and B are sentences, (b3) If A is an open sentence of L^N, then $Pi^N(A, B)$ is to be

$$\sum_{i=1}^{N} (w^N(W_i) \times Pi^N(A_i, B))$$

where W_i, $w^N(W_i)$, and A_i are as in (a2),

(b4) If A is an open sentence of L^∞, then $Pi^\infty(A, B)$ is to be

$$\underset{N \to \infty}{\text{Limit}} \sum_{i=1}^{N} (w^N(W_i) \times Pi^\infty(A_i, B)),$$

where W_i, $w^N(W_i)$, and A_i are as in (a2).

Strategies for estimating in the light of one closed sentence of L_N the truth-value in L^N of another closed sentence of L^N are readily arranged in a continuum, and the two strategies which lie at the opposite ends of that continuum are readily shown to pass the first five requirements in (b1) and fail the sixth one. On the strength of these two results, $Pi^N(A, B)$, where A and B are two closed sentences of L^N and where Pi^N is any function meeting all six of the requirements in (b1), is claimed to qualify as an estimate made in the light of B of the truth-value of A in L^N; and, more generally, $Pi(A, B)$, where A is a closed or an open sentence of L, where B is a closed sentence of L, and where Pi is defined as in (b1)–(b4), is claimed to qualify as an estimate made in the light of B of the statistical probability of A in L.

There is an alternative to (b1), namely: allotting weights to the state-descriptions of L^N; taking $Pi_0^N(A)$, the absolute inductive probability of A in L^N, to be the combined weights of the state-descriptions of L^N in which A holds; and taking $Pi^N(A, B)$ to be $Pi_0^N(A \& B)/Pi_0^N(B)$ when $Pi_0^N(B)$ is non-zero, 1 when $P_0^N(B)$ is zero. The various manners in which weights are currently allotted, (1) to the member of a probability set or, to phrase matters in sentence-theoretic terms, to the individual constants of L_0^N and (2), to the state-descriptions of L_0^N are briefly discussed; so is the possibility of letting the latter weights vary with the former, a departure from standard practice.

Comments on Leblanc Paper

by RICHARD C. JEFFREY

I HEARTILY endorse Leblanc's view that statistical and inductive probability functions ought to take the same sorts of arguments, although I (and perhaps Leblanc) attach no importance to the particular choice of sentences as arguments—propositions, construed perhaps as sets of possible eventualities, would do as well. Thus, one might attribute probability not to a sentence in a language L, but rather to the set of all those interpretations of the non-logical constants of L under which the sentence comes out true. But contrary to what Leblanc appears to believe, it is to such sets of possible eventualities, and not to sets of individuals, that statistical probabilities are commonly allotted, as in Kolmogorov's monograph of 1933, and in most textbooks, e.g., those of Feller and Loève. Consequently, I see no important difference between Leblanc's sentences and the "events" which probabilists generally take to be the arguments of probability functions. Of course, one can count noses, heads, or people with the same result; and similarly, in the particularly simple cases (e.g., some urn problems), in which there is a natural one-to-one correspondence between the individuals and the mutually exclusive, collectively exhaustive possible eventualities (Kolmogorov's *elementary events*) it is not unusual to hear the individuals, rather than the corresponding possible eventualities, being described as, say, equiprobable. But I think that in every case assignments of weights or of probabilities to the individuals of a language are reflections of a more fundamental assignment of probabilities to certain corresponding propositions or sentences about the individuals; and that if one changes the correspondence, e.g., by attributing different properties to the individuals, one may need to change the weights. Leblanc's acceptance of indistinguishability of some individuals as a ground for not attributing the same weights to all lends support to this position: indistinguishability *in L*, at any rate, depends on what properties are expressible in L.

Leblanc gives the following account of statistical probability. Weights are somehow assigned to the individuals or individual constants of L^N; the statistical probability of an open sentence with one free variable is identified with the sum of the weights of the individuals that satisfy the sentence; the statistical probability of an open sentence with $n > 1$ free variables is the sum of the weights of the ordered n-tuples that satisfy the sentence, where the weight of an n-tuple is taken to be the product of the weights of its members; and the statistical probability of a closed sentence is taken to be 1 or 0, accordingly as the sentence is true or false. In L^N, each individual is to get the same weight, $1/N$, unless some of the individuals are indistinguishable, in which case the weight of an individual is to be $1/ij$, where i is the number of equivalence classes into which the relation of indistinguishability divides the domain of individuals and j is the population of the equivalence class to which the individual in question belongs. Leblanc calls two individuals "indistinguishable *in L*" if each satisfies all and only the open sentences with one free variable that the other does. I find parts of this account unsatisfactory for the following reasons.

Ps, applied to closed sentences, does the work of the function, *the truth value of*, and therefore it does not do the (different) work of the function, *statistical probability of*, which I shall henceforth symbolize by "Po" (*for objective probability*), to avoid notational conflict with Leblanc. I identify Po as the function that is involved when gamblers talk about fairness of a die or a wheel and when engineers talk about the informational capacity of a noisy communication channel, and which is basic to much of genetics and statistical mechanics. For example, let the individuals $a_1, \ldots, a_N$ be the successive occasions on which a certain coin is tossed; let Ha_n be the proposition that the coin lands head up on the n-th of these occasions; and suppose, for definiteness, that the coin is lost after a_7, and never tossed again. It is natural to represent this situation in L^7, with "H" as a primitive predicate symbol. Now Po cannot be Ps, because it makes perfectly good sense to believe that $Po("Ha_n")$ is $1/2$ for each n from 1 to 7, and that

$$Po("Ha_1. \ldots .Ha_7") = 1/128,$$

whereas Ps assigns either 0 or 1 to each of these sentences. These are potentialities that Ps lacks and that Po has, if statistics, gambling, and much of science makes sense.

Nor can the situation be saved by interpreting $Po("Ha_n")$ as $Ps("Hx")$, for since the successive occasions on which the coin is tossed are all distinguishable, the individuals will all have the same weight, and the possible values of $Ps("Hx")$ will all be multiples of $1/7$; but $Po("Ha_n")$ may be $1/2$, or as close to $1/2$ as makes no odds.

The decision to count the weight of an ordered n-tuple of individuals as the product of the weights of its members (i.e., as $1/N^n$, if all individuals have the same weight) implies that "Ax", "By", ... are statistically independent, where A, B, ... are the primitive predicates of L^N. Leblanc realizes this fact, but seems indifferent to what I take to be its disastrous consequences: many of the stochastic processes that are important in science and engineering involve statistical dependencies (relative to Po) among atomic sentences of L, and I suppose that Leblanc would hope to represent these dependencies via dependencies among atomic open sentences, relative to Ps.

Although I judge Leblanc's account of statistical probability to be incorrect in various ways, his view that Pi(A, B) is some sort of estimate, based on the evidence B, of the statistical probability of A, seems tenable. Indeed, De Finetti bases his account of unknown (statistical) probabilities on the notion that, e.g., in the case of coin-tossing, $Po(H_1)$ is almost certainly

$$\lim_{n \to \infty} Pi(H_1, E_n)$$

where E_n is a complete report on the outcome of tosses number 2, ... , n and where Pi, for De Finetti, is subjective probability. But $Pi(H_1, E_n)$ cannot usefully be interpreted as an estimate of $Ps(H_1)$, which must be 0 or 1, whereas $\lim_{n \to \infty} Pi(H_1, E_n)$ may be 1/2. (Of course, $Pi(A, B)$ is the probability, relative to the evidence B, that $Ps(A)$ is 1, but this can hardly be what Leblanc means when he says that $Pi(A, B)$ is an estimate of $Ps(A)$.).

Finally, I do not see the point of the terms "at least passable" for functions that satisfy (a)–(e) of Section IV, and "at least fair" for those that satisfy (f) or (f′) as well. As Ramsey and De Finetti have shown any acceptable betting function must satisfy (a)–(f) and (f′) on pain of incoherence; i.e., on pain for the bettor of having a book made against him, so that with logical necessity he will suffer a net loss on some set of bets, each of which seems fair to him in that the odds are in agreement with his betting function. Then since an acceptable inductive probability measure ought to be a coherent betting function (among other things), I do not see the point of calling a function "passable" when it fails to satisfy (f) or (f′). Nor do I see the point of calling a function "fair" as an inductive probability measure when it merely satisfies (a)–(f) or (f′); for example, a function relative to which all atomic propositions are independent does not permit learning from experience and is therefore unacceptable as an inductive probability measure, even though it satisfies (a)–(f) or (f′). This objection is not merely terminological: the interest of the conclusions that Leblanc draws in Section IV evaporates when neutral terms, e.g., "of type 1" and "of type 2," are substituted for the misleadingly value-loaded "at least fair" and "at least passable."

Reply to Jeffrey

By LEBLANC

1. A GOOD many writers, as Professor Jeffrey points out, allot statistical probabilities only to sets of possible eventualities. Other writers,

however, (and Neyman is one) allot them to sets in general regardless of the make-up of those sets. I have accordingly placed no restriction—and still insist on placing none—on the kind of individuals which the individual constants of my languages L are to designate.

2. It may not be downright disastrous, as Professor Jeffrey suggests, to set the weight of an ordered n-tuple of individuals (or individual constants) at the product of the weights of the individuals (or individual constants) which make up the n-tuple. It is, however, unduly restrictive to do so and I am most willing to amend my treatment of open sentences on this point. Details will be found in my book *Statistical and Inductive Probabilities*.

3. Whether probability functions ought to take sentences or sets as their arguments may not matter. When, however sentences are given the nod, statistical probabilities prove to be truth-values of a sort and inductive ones to be estimates of truth-values and hence estimates of statistical probabilities. Statistical and inductive probabilities are thereby brought into close touch; so are probability and truth.

4. Sets, to be sure, are still in the running as arguments to statistical probability functions. Since, however, the sets to which statistical probabilities are allotted in the literature do not always consist of events, the statistical probability of a set cannot always be passed off as the probability of a so-called aggregate event (or set event). Among other interpretations on hand, I favor Neyman's, under which the statistical probability of a subset S of a probability set U is the probability of a member of U or, to be more prolix about it, of an unspecified member of U belonging to S. It inspired, by the way, my sentence-theoretic handling of statistical probabilities, free individual variables doing duty with me for Neyman's indefinite article "a." It also leaves room, I believe, for inductive probabilities. To restrict myself here (as Professor Jeffrey would) to events, the probability of an unspecified one of the events in a probability set U being one of the events in a subset S of U is one thing, the probability of a specific event (whatever set of events the event in question may belong to) quite another. I, for one, would construe the former as a statistical probability, the latter as an inductive one.

5. The weights I attach to the individual constants of L^N, the pairs made up of those constants, and so on, have unduly puzzled some members of this conference. They match the weights which statistical probability theorists attach to the members of their probability sets, the pairs made up of those members, and so on, and should cause no difficulty. The weight in L^N of an individual constant, say 'c' of L^N, being equal by definition to the statistical probability in L^N of the open sentence 'w = c'

simply proves to be the probability of an unspecified number of U_{LN} being c; that of a pair of individual constants, say $<$'c_1', 'c_2'$>$ of L^N, being equal to the statistical probability in L^N of the open sentence 'w $= c_1$ & x $= c_2$' proves to be the probability of an unspecified pair of members of U_{LN} being $<c_1, c_2>$; and so on. How the weights in question ought to be chosen was a controversial matter before I addressed myself to it and, I gather, remains one.

6. Professor Jeffrey objects to my calling the inductive probability functions which meet the first five of requirements (a)–(f) "at least fair," those which meet all six of them "at least passable," and so on. He may be right on this score. My point is merely this. (1) The two functions Pi' and Pi", diametrically opposed though they may be, meet the first five of requirements (a)–(f); any function which meets the same five requirements must therefore rate some consideration as a truth-value estimating function. (2) The two functions Pi' and Pi", extreme as they are, fail to meet the sixth one of requirements (a)–(f); any function which meets all six of requirements (a)–(f) must therefore rate some extra consideration as a truth-value estimating function. The point, when thus restated, may still be of some significance. I grant, of course, that many of the functions which meet all six of requirements (a)–(f) have shortcomings as truth-value estimating functions. Which ones do, which ones don't, is, however, a complicated question which cannot be settled in a line or two.

Discussion on Leblanc Paper

(Based on notes taken by HARRY TARTAR and STEPHEN BARKER)

JEFFREY: You leave it an open question how weights are to be assigned to individuals: will you indicate what considerations would enter when we try to decide how to assign weights?

LEBLANC: I favor assigning equal weights to all individual constants and equal weights to state descriptions; though the case of indistinguishability discussed in the paper would provide an exception. At any rate it is a rational a priori matter, not an empirical one.

BAR-HILLEL: Are unequal weights ever assigned to individuals in practice?

LEBLANC: Yes; unequal weights are assigned in modern treatments of probabilistic questions, both theoretical and practical, but I can only cite the case of indistinguishability for justifying such unequal assignments.

BAR-HILLEL: What do you mean by individuals?

LEBLANC: Anything that can have a name.

BAR-HILLEL: Whereas you treat inductive probabilities always as estimates of relative frequencies, Carnap regards them only sometimes as such. I feel that your procedure trivializes the problem.

LEBLANC: My procedure is of interest because it achieves some unification of two rival schools, by showing that both kinds of probability can be assigned to sentences, and also by interpreting both statistical and inductive probability as involving truth values.

KYBURG: How much unification have you achieved? It would seem that the logical theorists would say that weights must be assigned a priori and the frequency theorists would assign weights on the basis of observed frequencies.

BRAITHWAITE: For example, it is a matter of very high level empirical hypothesis to choose between Bose-Einstein and Fermi-Dirac statistics.

BLACK: I admire the mathematical elegance of your paper, but I feel that it leaves untouched the philosophic issues mentioned by Ernest Nagel in his opening address. It gives us no idea of the meaning of probability or induction. Besides, people are tempted to draw misleading inferences from such treatments of the subject. To speak of the "probability of an individual" is unfortunate, and can only be a misleading way of speaking about the probability of an event. When you use the word "probability" we think of probability in the ordinary sense; perhaps you should speak instead of attaching "Leblanc numbers" to individuals. But then we would know that we were being left in the dark as to what these things are supposed to be. Your use of the word "individual" was also misleading.

ANDERSON (ALAN): Perhaps the word "element" could be used instead.

BRAITHWAITE: I am interested in your results, but I am primarily interested in having an explanation of the connection between statistical probabilities and betting quotients. I find it difficult to understand what Keynes and Jeffreys meant by calling probability a logical relation; Carnap's theory seems an elegant exercise but hard to apply; the frequency theory is not satisfactory for some interpretations. So I have been attracted by the subjective theories of Ramsey, De Finetti, and Savage. But one great difficulty with the subjective theory which treats probabilities as betting quotients is that it is difficult to attach a betting quotient to a hypothesis. De Finetti allows bets only on specific events. Savage allows us to bet on hypotheses being true; but what is the event we are then betting on? Does your treatment give some roundabout sense to the notion of a betting quotient for a hypothesis? Is what we are betting on, that a particular set of marks would be accepted by a scientist?

MORGENBESSER: All this seems like Peirce's view that what you are betting on is the view which science is destined to hold if inquiry is carried to its ultimate limit.

BRAITHWAITE: This ideal is mythical; the ideal scientist is the one who knows the truth, and this cannot be gotten by extrapolation from existing science.

BAR-HILLEL: On the betting-quotient interpretation there is no real behavioristic difference between the infinite case and one limited, say, to a million events. I find more troublesome the transition in subjective theories from talk about betting quotients to talk of "fair" betting quotients.

BRAITHWAITE (to BAR-HILLEL): It is "my estimate of the probability" that is involved, and I try to make this accord with the "objective probability," which does obey the axioms set forth for "fair" betting quotients.

MCCULLOCH: We should speak here of "guestimates."

LEBLANC: I prefer to interpret inductive probabilities as estimates of truth values or functions of such, to avoid subjective interpretations of the betting-quotient type.

JEFFREY: The subjective theory has something more to offer than mere "hunch." It is a neutral theory. If you were fortunate enough to know the statistical probability you would adopt it as your subjective probability. Therefore the Ramsey-De Finetti arguments apply to statistical probability measures, and require them to satisfy all six of Leblanc's requirements, to count as fair.

LEBLANC: It would be better to speak of "coherent" betting quotients than of "fair" ones.

BAR-HILLEL: In many situations the relevant evidence is not of an exclusively statistical nature, but may be of many different kinds.

BRAITHWAITE: This is the strength of my position; I should wish my estimate to correspond with the objective situation. Even in the case of a unique event—as the next throw of *that* coin—I am actually betting as if it were a member of a class of similar coins.

BAR-HILLEL: Would this be true in the case of the pressing of the button of an Atlas missile?

BRAITHWAITE: Certainly.

JEFFREY: There is a problem in deciding which coins are to be taken as sufficiently similar.

BRAITHWAITE: The tests you use are those of the statisticians—their acceptance and rejection tests.

NAGEL (to BRAITHWAITE): What do you think the prospects are for interpreting Probability$_1$ of univeral hypotheses as "estimates"?

BRAITHWAITE: Leblanc shows one line of approach.

BLACK: There are two approaches: in one case you are betting on a unique event; in the other you are betting on a series of approximations, where the limit would have the value o in the infinite case.

BRAITHWAITE: The law must be stated in such a way that the parameter lies within a certain range.

LEBLANC: We could add axioms so that the probability would not tend toward o.

BAR-HILLEL: We do not need a full interpretation of probability—a partial one would do; fair betting quotient is one such partial interpretation.

BRAITHWAITE: What is the sense of "partial" interpretation?

BAR-HILLEL: Approximately the one discussed by Carnap in "The Methodological Character of Theoretical Concepts" in *Minnesota Studies in the Philosophy of Science*, volume one, 1956.

II

On Vindicating Induction

by WESLEY C. SALMON

ALTHOUGH the process of mathematical idealization applied to empirical reality may not be perfectly understood as yet, there can be no doubt of its utility in science and in the logical analysis of scientific method. The philosophical theory of probability which identifies probabilities with limits of relative frequencies in infinite sequences of events certainly involves such idealization. I wish to take this idealization as a point of departure, setting aside the problems connected with the idealization as such. I shall assume, therefore, that when we are dealing with probabilities we are often dealing with large aggregates of events which can reasonably be treated as if they were infinite ordered sequences. I shall assume further that it would be desirable, if possible, to have a way of inferring the value of the limit of the relative frequency of an attribute in this type of infinite sequence. The problem is an inductive problem. Clearly we are concerned with the type of sequence in which our inferences must be based upon observational data, in particular, observation of the relative frequency of the attribute in some finite initial portion of the sequence. Whether or not there exists, in an abstract sense, a mathematical rule governing the development of the sequence, no such rule is available to us as part of our data. The problem to which I shall address myself is the problem of selecting and justifying a rule to govern the inference from a statement about the relative frequency in a finite initial section of a sequence to a statement of the value of the limit of the relative frequency in that sequence. This is precisely the problem Reichenbach attempted to solve with his "pragmatic justification" of induction.[1]

There have been many criticisms of Reichenbach's argument, but the crucial one, it seems to me, is one of which he was quite aware. By his own admission, the same argument which he uses to justify his *rule of induction*

[1] H. Reichenbach, *The Theory of Probability*, Berkeley, University of California Press, 1959, sec. 87.

justifies equally well any other rule in an infinite class of "asymptotic rules." He attempted to resolve this difficulty by arguing that, since the results given by all of these asymptotic rules converge in the long run to the same value when they are applied to the same sequence of events, we are justified in selecting his *rule of induction* on grounds of "descriptive simplicity."[2] This argument is faulty. Although the rules do, as he says, converge, they do not converge uniformly. As a matter of fact, the class of asymptotic rules contains rules such that, for any observed relative frequency in an initial section of any finite length and for any arbitrarily selected real number between zero and one inclusive, there exists an asymptotic rule permitting the inference of that real number as the value of the limit on the basis of the given observed frequency.[3] This means that the asymptotic rules are not in any sense empirically equivalent. On Reichenbach's own grounds, then, descriptive simplicity cannot be considered as a basis for selecting one rule from the infinite class of asymptotic rules. As long as this objection to Reichenbach's pragmatic justification stands, any other objections seem to me to be superfluous.

Another set of considerations can be introduced. Let A be any reference class (ordered sequence) of events and let $B_1, \ldots, B_k$ be attributes which are mutually exclusive and exhaustive within A. Let $F^n(A, B_i)$ be the relative frequency with which B_i occurs in A up to and including the nth place in the sequence. Simple arithmetical considerations yield the following conclusions:

$$(1) \qquad \sum_{i=1}^{k} F^n(A, B_i) = 1, \text{ for every n}$$

$$(2) \qquad 0 \leq F^n(A, B_i) \leq 1, \text{ for every n}$$

$$(3) \qquad \sum_{i=1}^{k} \lim_{n \to \infty} F^n(A, B_i) = 1$$

$$(4) \qquad 0 \leq \lim_{n \to \infty} F^n(A, B_i) \leq 1$$

Any rule, asymptotic or otherwise, for inferring from the relative frequency in an initial section to the limit of the relative frequency can be characterized in the following manner:

---

[2] *Ibid.*, p. 447.

[3] W. Salmon, "The Predictive Inference," *Philosophy of Science*, vol. 24, 2 (April, 1957).

(5)
From $\qquad F^n(A, B_i) = m_i/n$

to infer $\qquad \lim_{n \to \infty} F^n(A, B_i) = m_i/n + f(x_1, \ldots, x_r)$

where the nature of the arguments $x_1, \ldots, x_r$ of the function f is, for the moment, purposely left unspecified. By virtue of (3) and (4), in order to avoid selecting rules which will lead to self-contradictory conclusions, the following *normalizing conditions* must be imposed upon our rules:

(6) $\qquad 0 \leq m_i/n + f(x_1, \ldots, x_r) \leq 1$

(7) $\qquad \sum_{i=1}^{k} [m_i/n + f(x_1, \ldots, x_r)] = 1$

These conditions must be satisfied for each value of n $(n = 1, 2, 3, \ldots)$; otherwise, for some n our rule would permit an inference to a self-contradictory conclusion on the basis of a sample of that size.

Unfortunately the normalizing conditions alone will not solve the problem of finding a unique rule, for there are infinitely many asymptotic rules which satisfy these conditions. This infinite class of rules exhibits the kind of non-uniform convergence mentioned above.[4]

There is, however, still a further condition which may be placed upon rules of the type being considered.[5] In order to state this condition it is necessary to explain what is meant by a *purely linguistic difference* between two expressions. We shall say that two expressions in a given language have a *purely linguistic difference* (or alternatively that they differ by a *purely linguistic transformation*) if their equivalence follows from the syntactical and semantical rules of that language. If the expressions are propositional or sentential expressions, the equivalance of which I speak is material equivalence. If the expressions are class expressions, the relevant equivalence is class identity. If the expressions are predicates, equivalence consists in having the same extension. The notion of a purely linguistic difference can be extended to the case of expressions in different languages in a very natural way. Two expressions in two different languages have a purely linguistic difference if their equivalence can be demonstrated in a metalanguage

---

[4] *Ibid.*

[5] The discussion of the *criterion of linguistic invariance* follows closely a discussion of W. Salmon, "Vindication of Induction," in Feigl and Maxwell, editors, *Current Issues in Philosophy of Science*, New York, Holt, Rinehart & Winston, 1961. In this article the criterion is applied to confirmation functions as well as inductive rules.

containing the semantics and syntax of both languages. The following two examples illustrate what is meant by a purely linguistic difference:

1. The statement that a certain bar of iron is thirty-six inches long differs purely linguistically from the statement that the same bar of iron is at the same moment three feet long.

2. If a new predicate, "rend," is introduced which is equivalent by definition to the predicate "both round and red," then the statement "x is rend" differs purely linguistically from the statement "x is both round and red."

However, even if it should happen, as matter of fact, that the class of featherless bipeds contains the same members as the class of rational animals, the statement, "Socrates is a featherless biped," would *not* differ purely linguistically from the statement, "Socrates is a rational animal," for the identity of the two classes does not follow from syntactical and semantical considerations alone.

I think it is fundamental to theory of probability and induction that we recognize and adopt a certain *principle of invariance with respect to purely linguistic transformations*. This principle, roughly stated, asserts that probability relations, relations of confirmation, and relations of inductive support are not functions of purely linguistic considerations. The principle in turn gives rise to a criterion of adequacy for inductive methods or rules; I call it the *criterion of linguistic invariance*. It places the following requirement upon inductive rules:

> Whenever two inductive inferences are made according to the same rule, if the premises of the one differ purely linguistically from the premises of the other, then the conclusion of the one must not contradict the conclusion of the other.

This criterion is obviously a consistency requirement; violations of it are cases in which an inductive rule permits contradictory conclusions to be derived from the same evidence. The contradiction in question may, so to speak, bridge two languages, but that does not make it any less objectionable.

The force of this criterion may be illustrated by reference to the preceding examples. If, in a scientific experiment, the result that a certain bar of iron is thirty-six inches long confirms some hypothesis to a certain degree, then the criterion requires that the result that the same bar of iron is three feet long must confirm that same hypothesis to the same degree. Similarly, suppose we have observed that the ratio of A's in a particular sample which are both red and round is m/n. It follows, of course, that the ratio of A's in the same sample which are rend is also m/n. If an inductive rule permitted us to infer from the fact that m/n A's are red and round that the limit of the relative frequency of things being red and round in A is p, and if the same inductive rule permitted us to infer from the fact that m/n A's (in the same sample) are rend that the limit of the relative frequency of things being both red and round in A is q, where p ≠ q, this rule would violate the criterion.

The criterion of linguistic invariance strikes me as being eminently reasonable; indeed, almost trivially so. There is, I think, only one possible alternative to adopting it, and that alternative is to maintain that there exists one particular privileged language of science whose special status can be established a priori. If this were the case, then there would be no need for a criterion of linguistic invariance for there would be no occasion to translate statements from the privileged language into an inferior one. This view has, I think, nothing to recommend it; it involves the most egregious sort of metaphysics. If such metaphysics is to be avoided, the criterion of linguistic invariance must be adopted.

Let us see what can be accomplished by application of the criterion of linguistic invariance, utilizing at the same time the normalizing conditions set out above. Since the normalizing conditions, as stated, must be satisfied for every value of n, we will proceed with the argument for cases in which n has some fixed value. In order to carry out this task we must examine the function f which appears in the general characterization of inductive rules, and we must pay particular attention to the arguments $x_1, \ldots, x_r$ of this function. Two facts are immediately apparent. The quantities i and k cannot be arguments of the function f, for these quantities are subject to change by a purely linguistic transformation. The variable i is the index variable for the predicates; the value of i attached to a given attribute can be changed by a mere reordering of the predicates. If the inferred value of the limit of the relative frequency of an attribute were a function of i, this inferred value would not be linguistically invariant. (One might, I suppose, seek to escape this conclusion by making i the index of the attributes themselves, rather than the predicates. This procedure would amount to mentioning specific attributes in the inductive rules, and this, in turn, is tantamount to adopting a privileged language of science—an alternative already rejected.) A similar consideration applies to k, the number of predicates in our exclusive and exhaustive set. This number can be changed by the trivial linguistic transformation of definining two new predicates which are mutually exclusive and whose disjunction is equivalent to one of the predicates in the original set—that is, define $B_{i'}$ and $B_{i''}$ so that $B_i = B_{i'}$ v $B_{i''}$. Again, if the inferred value of the limit of the relative frequency of some attribute were a function of k, this inferred value could be changed by the foregoing sort of purely linguistic transformation.

There is one remaining possibility to be considered. Can f be a function of m_i alone? Since we are dealing with cases in which n is fixed, it is equivalent to consider what happens if f is a function of m_i/n alone. Utilizing the normalizing conditions it is easy to show that $f(m_i/n)$ must be identically zero.

1. Consider the case in which $k = n$; there are the same number of attributes as there are members of the sample. Suppose further that $m_i = 1$ for each i; that is, each attribute occurs once in the sample. By (7),

$$\sum_{i=1}^{k} [1/n + f(1/n)] = k [1/n + f(1/n)] = 1 + kf(1/n) = 1.$$

Hence $\qquad\qquad\qquad f(1/n) = 0.$

2. It can now be shown that $f(m_i/n) = 0$ for any possible value of m_i. Let m_1 have any value such that $0 \leq m_1 \leq n$. Let $m_i = 1$ for $i = 2, 3, \ldots,$ k; that is, we are considering the case in which B_1 occurs an arbitrary number of times m_1 in our sample and each other attribute occurs just once. We have

$$\sum_{i=1}^{k} [m_i/n + f(m_i/n)] = \sum_{i=1}^{k} m_i/n + f(m_1/n) + \sum_{i=2}^{k} f(1/n) = 1.$$

By (1),

$$\sum_{i=1}^{k} m_i/n = 1.$$

We have just proved that $f(1/n) = 0.$

Hence, $\qquad\qquad\qquad f(m_i/n) = 0.$

There is one inductive rule characterized by the condition that the function f is identically zero; this is the Reichenbach rule of induction. We have just shown that no other rule beside this one can fulfill both the normalizing conditions and the criterion of linguistic invariance. We have considered the possible functional dependency of inferred values of limits upon n, m_i, i, and k; these are the only variables which appear in the statement of the normalizing conditions. The argument thus proves that there is at most one consistent rule for inferring values of limits of relative frequencies from observed initial portions. A violation of either the normalizing conditions or the criterion of linguistic invariance by a rule means, as has been noted, that the rule can give rise to inconsistency.

The natural question at this point is whether the rule of induction is a consistent rule. Quite obviously it cannot violate the normalizing conditions. But does it meet the criterion of linguistic invariance? Unfortunately it does not as things stand.[6] This point is demonstrated by a version of the Goodman paradox, a paradox which may appear rather trivial but which turns out to be profound and difficult.[7]

If we have observed a large number of emeralds and found them all to be green, by the rule of induction we would be entitled to infer that all emeralds are green. Now, let t be some specified future time (e.g., the beginning of the twenty-first century) and let the predicate "grue" be defined so that it applies to things examined before t which are green and it applies to things examined after t which are blue. Similarly, let the predicate "bleen" be defined so that it applies to things examined before t which are blue and it applies to things examined after t which are green. According to the definition of "grue," the above-mentioned observations may equally well be described by the statement that all observed emeralds are grue. From this evidence we are entitled, by the rule of induction, to conclude that all emeralds are grue. This conclusion contradicts the former conclusion that all emeralds are green. In this paradox we have something very close to a violation of the criterion of linguistic invariance.

The immediate intuitive reaction to this paradox is to say that there is something peculiar about the predicates "grue" and "bleen," in particular that they are time-dependent predicates. As Goodman has carefully pointed out, however, this intuition is not easy to justify. It is true, of course, that "grue" and "bleen" are positional—i.e., involve explicit reference to the time t—if "green" and "blue" are taken as basic predicates in terms o which they are defined. However, if "grue" and "bleen" are taken as basic, then "green" and "blue" exhibit this peculiarity. In this case, "green"

---

[6] This objection is stated by S. Barker in his comments upon the article cited in footnote 5. These comments appear in the same volume.

[7] N. Goodman, *Fact, Fiction, and Forecast*, Cambridge, Harvard University Press, 1955, pp. 74 ff.

would be defined so as to apply to things examined before t which are grue and to things examined after t which are bleen. "Blue" would be defined analogously. In view of this symmetry it is difficult to see in what sense we could say that "grue" and "bleen" are time-dependent predicates while "blue" and "green" are not.

The foregoing formulation of the paradox is essentially that given by Goodman; for our purposes this formulation has certain shortcomings. First, the Goodman formulation does not actually involve a violation of the criterion of linguistic invariance, for the equivalence of the two premises, "All observed emeralds are green" and "All observed emeralds are grue," does not depend solely upon the definitions of the predicates, but also upon the synthetic statement that the observations occur prior to the specified time t. Second, temporal positionality is not the only kind of positionality possible; it is desirable to characterize positionality more generally. Third, there is basic ambiguity in the definitions of "grue" and "bleen." Let us reformulate the paradox in a way which will repair these difficulties.[8] Let the universe be taken as an ordered sequence $x_1, x_2, \ldots ,$ where it is understood that each x_1 represents an object of reasonably small spatial and temporal dimensions. "Green" and "blue" have their customary meanings. We choose some subscript, say 1,000, and give the following definititions:

x_i is grue $=_{df} x_i$ is green and $i \leq 1,000$ or x_i is blue and $i > 1,000$.

x_i is bleen $=_{df} x_i$ is blue and $i \leq 1,000$ or x_i is green and $i > 1,000$.

Obviously, "green" and "blue" are again definable in terms of "grue" and "bleen," and when so defined they become positional predicates. Now, if we take the two premises:

x_1 is an emerald which is green, x_2 is an emerald which

is green, ... , x_{100} is an emerald which is green

and

x_1 is an emerald which is grue, x_2 is an emerald which

is grue, ... , x_{100} is an emerald which is grue

there is a purely linguistic difference between them. The standard inductive rule permits two conclusions which are mutually contradictory on the

[8] The reformulation is suggested in R. Carnap, "On the Application of Inductive Logic," *Philosophy and Phenomenological Research*, vol. 8, (1947), p. 133.

assumption that the class of emeralds is not exhausted before the 1,000th place:

For every i, if x_i is an emerald then x_i is green

and

For every i, if x_i is an emerald then x_i is grue

Two questions arise from this paradox. First, is there any important sense in which Goodman's predicates are time dependent or positional and the ordinary color predicates are not? If the answer is affirmative, the second question arises. Can we give good reasons for treating these time-dependent predicates in a special way which will prevent violations of the criterion of linguistic invariance? There is danger in ignoring the second question. We might find what appears to be an important asymmetry between the Goodman-type predicates and the normal predicates; it might then be very tempting to exploit this asymmetry just for the sake of escaping the Goodman paradox. For example, the Goodman-type predicates are time dependent with respect to the predicates of ordinary language. This is a genuine asymmetry. However, it would seem to me to be pointless to exclude the Goodman-type predicates from our language on this ground, even though it would avoid the Goodman paradox on the basis of a genuine asymmetry. The question would remain: is there any good reason for according the ordinary predicates such a privileged status? Might not a language with extraordinary basic predicates be equally adequate, for all we know, for the purposes of science?

Before attempting any answer to these questions I should like to present the problem in still different terms. As I conceive the problem of induction, it is the problem of finding grounds for selecting a unique rule of inductive inference from the infinity of possible rules. This problem cannot, however, be treated without paying close attention to the predicates involved. The selection of an inductive rule implies, of course, the exclusion of many alternative rules. The difficulty is that there is a degree of symmetry between the selection of an inductive rule and the selection of predicates to which this rule is to be applied. If we select a particular rule but allow its free application to every type of predicate that can possibly be defined, this is tantamount to allowing the use of other inductive rules besides the one selected. The introduction of the Goodman-type predicates which are positional with respect to the normal predicates into a language which utilizes the standard inductive rule has precisely the effect of introducing a conflicting inductive rule. We must, therefore, pay close attention to the sort of language to be used in conjunction with rules of inductive inference. Two difficulties are to be avoided. First, we shall attempt to exclude violations of the criterion of linguistic invariance which arise by allowing complete latitude with respect to the admission of predicates. Second, we shall attempt to preserve the principle of linguistic invariance by refusing to elevate one language with its particular set of predicates to a privileged position. To avoid these two extremes it is necessary to examine the types of language appropriate to inductive inference. This is best accomplished, I think, by considering the manner in which an inductive logic can be developed.

There are many good reasons for regarding an inductive logic as an extension of a deductive logic. Undoubtedly there are many different ways of providing the extension, but it seems to me that the fundamental feature of the extension is the addition to the apparatus of deductive logic of an inductive rule. A deductive logic may be regarded as a formal system containing logical constants, variables of various types, and non-logical constants among its symbols. In the usual manner it will have formation rules, axioms, and rules of immediate deductive inference. If the system has been constructed in the desired way, the rules of immediate inference have the important characteristic of being truth-preserving in any standard interpretation of the system. An inductive rule will not have the truth-preserving characteristic.

It is not necessary to go into great detail concerning the structure of the deductive system underlying inductive logic. The deductive system should be very generously endowed. It should be rich enough to contain whatever mathematics we need for natural science, including the probability calculus. Furthermore, it should contain ample supplies of individual and functional constants and variables. The individual and functional constants will, of course, be uninterpreted; they will comprise the vocabulary which is to become the basic descriptive vocabulary of the system when interpretation occurs.

When we consider adding an inductive rule, such as the Reichenbach rule of induction, to this system, we immediately face the prospect of making it inconsistent. This is the essential point of the Goodman paradox. Our problem is to introduce the rule and restrict it in such a way as to avoid contradiction. No doubt this can be done in a purely syntactical manner, but if we are to find a solution which is not completely *ad hoc* certain non-syntactical considerations must be taken into account. In particular, we must recognize the purposes for which the system is being developed. There are two primary ones, and they are not independent of one another. First, the language is designed to be a descriptive language; it must be capable of expressing true or false factual assertions. This means that the non-logical constants must be interpreted so as to refer to empirical reality. Second, the language is designed to incorporate inductive inference, so it must be supplemented with an inductive rule.

Let us first consider the matter of interpretation. It is quite clear that it cannot be achieved by interdefining the non-logical constants among themselves. We are all aware of the circularity involved in this procedure. Semantic rules of the following sort could be introduced:

"a" denotes Smith

"F" denotes yellow

This procedure is efficacious only if the metalanguage has already achieved reference for terms such as "Smith" and "yellow." Utilizing such rules would only push the same problem into the metalanguage. The alternative is to recognize that at some level of language we must provide the reference of terms by means of non-verbal definitions, and we might as well do it at the object language level. By non-verbal definition I mean semantic rules which establish directly some sort of referential relationship between symbols and non-linguistic entities as opposed to rules which establish only relationships among symbols of various languages. It is not necessary, of course, that all non-logical constants be interpreted by non-verbal rules, but only that a basic set be so interpreted.

There is no particular difficulty in providing non-verbal rules of reference for individual constants. One may simply indicate an object presented to the senses and decide to let an individual constant denote it. Ostensive definition is required for the interpretation of functional constants. For simplicity of statement I shall confine attention to singulary functional constants; the extension to n-ary functional constants is obvious. An ostensive definition contains three parts:

1. The indication of a number of positive instances, i.e., individuals which have the property to be denoted by that constant.

2. The indication of a number of negative instances, i.e., individuals which lack the property to be denoted by that constant.

3. A similarity clause stating that anything resembling all of the positive instances in some respect, provided it does not also resemble any of the

negative instances in that respect, also has the property to be denoted by that constant.

I shall now define a *purely ostensive predicate* as one which has the following characteristics:

1. It *can* be defined ostensively. (How it is, in fact, defined is immaterial.)

2. Its positive and negative instances for ostensive definition *can* be indicated non-verbally.

3. The respect in which the positive instances resemble each other and differ from the negative instances is open to direct inspection, i.e., the resemblance in question is an observable resemblance.

Purely ostensive predicates have at least two fundamentally important characteristics—they are observation predicates and they are open predicates. The sense in which they are observation predicates is obvious. They are open predicates in the sense that their definition does not limit the number of individuals to which they may be correctly applied. It may be, as a matter of fact, that a purely ostensive predicate applies correctly to, say, seventeen individuals only, but this cannot be a consequence of the definition alone.

The language of empirical science requires, I believe, a basic set of open observation predicates. These are needed in order to make that language capable of expressing the descriptive generalizations which play an indispensible role in explanation and prediction. These predicates must be given meaning in some manner which provides them with empirical reference. Purely ostensive predicates seem to be admirably suited to fulfill this function, and I do not know of any other kind of predicate which is thus well suited. I take it that a primary aim of induction is to furnish a method of establishing universal or statistical generalizations on the basis of observational evidence. For this to be possible we need open observation predicates in our descriptive language. I propose, therefore, that a semantic restriction be placed upon the interpretation of basic predicates; namely, that they be interpreted in such a way as to become purely ostensive predicates.

The next step is to show that the Goodman-type predicates are not purely ostensive predicates.[9] This point is rather obvious. If we examine a number of grue things at about the time t (referring to Goodman's formulation of the paradox), some just before and some just after, we will see

---

[9] I am indebted to Professor S. Körner for pointing this fact out to me.

that they do not look alike. Those examined before t will look different from those examined after t. Goodman has acknowledged that not all grue things match each other, but he regards this feature of the predicate "grue" as too *ad hoc* to be of any significance.[10] It seems to me that he is mistaken in thinking this fact to be lacking in deep significance, for it is this fact which implies that "grue" cannot be ostensively defined. It is clearly impossible to cite a number of positive instances of grue things and stipulate that anything which resembles them in some observational characteristic is grue. To be sure, all grue things resemble each other in being grue, but this is not a resemblance with respect to an observational characteristic. Although grue things resemble each other in being grue, they do not look alike.

If I am correct in thinking that open concepts referring to observational characteristics whose meaning can be specified by non-verbal definition stand in a fundamental position in the development of a descriptive language of science, then I think we can say that the Goodman-type predicates are ruled out from the possibility of playing this fundamental role. This is by no means to say that they must be ruled out of the scientific vocabulary entirely. Rather, their position is secondary and they are time dependent with respect to the fundamental predicates—those which are purely ostensive. Goodman has argued for a complete symmetry with respect to positionality between his predicates and the normal predicates. If his predicates are taken as basic, he says, then the normal predicates become positional when defined in terms of them. The answer I am offering amounts to saying that his predicates cannot be taken as basic in the descriptive language of science because they are not purely ostensive. In this way the symmetry is destroyed.

Reichenbach has placed considerable emphasis upon his distinction between primitive and advanced knowledge, insisting that the problem of justification of induction he was attempting to solve is a problem in primitive knowledge.[11] Although he has drawn this distinction in psychologistic terms and has been criticized for so doing, it seems to me to be an important distinction which can be made in logical terms.[12] A primitive inductive

[10] N. Goodman, "Positionality and Pictures," *Philosophical Review*, vol. 49, 4 (Oct., 1960).

[11] Reichenbach, *op. cit.*, p. 364.

[12] Barker, *op. cit.*, exemplifies this type of objection.

inference is one whose premises are observation statements alone. A primitive inductive rule is one which requires no premises which cannot be observation statements. If the Reichenbach rule of induction is to be taken as a primitive rule, then we can place the qualification upon it that the variables A and B_1 which appear in it must have their range restricted to purely ostensive predicates. With this restriction the Goodman paradox is eliminated in connection with the rule of induction.

We must now ask whether any violations of the criterion of linguistic invariance can arise with respect to the rule of induction. I think the answer is demonstrably negative. It is to be noted, first of all, that the inferred value of the limit of the relative frequency is a function of the observed relative frequency in an initial portion of the sequence in question. This quantity is linguistically invariant; regardless of how the reference class and attribute class are described, the numerical value remains unchanged. In order for a violation of linguistic invariance to occur it would be necessary that there be two classes which, *by definition*, coincide in part and fail to coincide in part. More exactly, there must be two classes F and G which have the following relationship: F and G can be partitioned on the basis of their definitions into two non-empty mutually exlcusive subsets, F_1, F_2, G_1, G_2, such that $F_1 = G_1$ while F_2 and G_2 have no members in common. Furthermore, this partitioning must be possible on a positional basis; the predicates characterizing the classes F and G must be relatively positional But, it is evident that not both F and G can be characterized by purely ostensive predicates. Hence, no violation of linguistic invariance can occur.

If the argument up to this point has been satisfactory we have succeeded in eliminating all inductive rules except one from the competition, and we have shown further that the one remaining rule is not subject to rejection on the grounds of the criterion of linguistic invariance. Does this constitute a vindication of that remaining rule?[13] Not quite, I believe. It remains to be shown that there is any positive reason for adopting the rule of induction, over and above the negative fact that it cannot be excluded as a rule which leads to contradiction. The argument requires two steps. First, it must be shown that it would be useful to be able to infer limits of relative frequencies if it is possible to do so. Keeping in mind the fact that a mathematical idealization is involved in talking about infinite sequences of

---

[13] I use the term "vindication" in the sense introduced by H. Feigl, "De Principiil Non Disputandum ...?" in M. Black, editor, *Philosophical Analysis*, Ithaca, Cornels University Press, 1950.

empirical events, I shall assume that such an aim is worth while. Second, it is necessary to show that the rule of induction is a rule somehow suited to accomplish this aim. Here, I think, Reichenbach's argument is now effective.[14] If the sequence in question has a limit of the relative frequency, repeated application of the rule of induction will achieve inference to the value of the limit within any desired degree of accuracy. If the sequence has no limit, no rule can provide any correct inference concerning its value.

[14] Reichenbach, op. cit., sec. 91.

Comments on Salmon Paper

By Max Black

In this, as in other recent papers, Professor Salmon has shown great resourcefulness in defending Peirce and Reichenbach's idea of a "pragmatic justification" of induction. Salmon's introduction of the notion of a "regular rule" that is linguistically invariant is an ingenious way of countering the known objections to the arbitrariness of such a "vindication." I cannot see that he has overcome these objections.

The proposed "vindication" is modest in its pretensions, pleading only that we have nothing to lose by following the inductive procedures recommended and unable to promise any likelihood of success. As Reichenbach said, "The conclusion of the inductive inference [as Salmon and he understand such an inference] cannot be proved to be true; and we may add that it cannot even be proved to be probable."[1] Vindication of induction will seem worth attempting only to those who, like Reichenbach, believe that knowledge about matters of fact is impossible and share his conviction that "the aim of knowing the future is unattainable."[2] If this is so, knowledge about the past and indeed about anything except the immediately observable is also unattainable. It is for this reason that Reichenbach calls the estimates of limiting frequencies of occurrence of a designated attribute in an infinite series (henceforward abbreviated to "$l.f.$'s") "blind posits." By a "posit" he means something like a bet or a wager, and by a blind posit such a bet made in total ignorance of any relevant data bearing upon the truth of the posit. Salmon, I believe, is trying to defend such posits. Reichenbach says that "a posit is a statement with which we deal as true, although the truth-value is unknown."[3] On the view under discussion, the value of the $l.f.$ is not merely unknown—it is, and must forever be, unknowable. The $l.f.$ of the occurrence of heads in a series of tosses with a given penny will be unknowable, because the penny will not be tossed infinitely often and would eventually become biased if this were tried. Pennies, like men, are mortal. And even if our views about "idealization" are as tolerant as Salmon's seem to be, we can never be in a position of *knowing* that we are in the neighborhood of the hypothetical $l.f.$ of the imaginary series. The position is, therefore, that we are to make predictions based on the relative frequency of occurrence (here after abbreviated to "$r.f.$") of the designated attribute in the observed initial

---

[1] *The Theory of Probability*, p. 475.   [2] *Op. cit.*, p. 480.
[3] *Op. cit.*, p. 373.

segment of the series, knowing that our predictions cannot be true, but with the sole assurance that *if* an *l.f.* exists we shall eventually come to make blind posits that are in its neighborhood—though we shall never know that we have reached such a point. A man would have to be a determined gambler to believe all this and still "deal" with the estimated *l.f.* "as true"; the position under defense seems to have no advantages over the unqualified skepticism with respect to matters of fact it is recommended as ameliorating. Better the honest skepticism of Hume than the false comfort of a pragmatic justification.

I hold such labels as "pragmatic justification" and "vindication" to be misleading and question-begging, for the reasons sketched above. We might reasonably talk about pragmatic justification in such cases as the following (similar to those Reichenbach himself invokes): (1) Knowing that neither of two roads facing me at an intersection has a better chance of getting me to my desired destination, I take the one with the easier gradient. (2) A surgeon, assured that his patient will die if no operation is performed, decides to operate, though the chance of success is slight, on the principle of there being "nothing to lose." Action of this sort, in the face of ignorance, is properly based upon and justified by *knowledge*, partial though it may be, of relevant data.

In a condition of *total* ignorance, such as "vindication" of inductive procedures assumes, *no* rational action is possible, and one guess or blind posit, if that label seems more reassuring, is as groundless as any other. The supposed analogy between the procedures that Salmon is defending and anything that deserves to be called pragmatic justification breaks down irremediably at the very outset. It is worth adding that the supposed "self-correcting" feature of the recommended procedure is a delusion. In a genuinely self-correcting procedure, such as that used in approximating the roots of an equation, each new step depends upon and requires its predecessor and is in some sense *better*, inasmuch as it brings us nearer to an existing goal. But in Salmon's procedure each estimate is discarded and has no bearing upon the postulated *l.f.*, since *anything* we observe in the "short run" is compatible with *any* value of the *l.f.* An equally good rule would be to make no estimates for a long time and only then to begin to compute *r.f.*'s.

Salmon makes a plausible case for his contention that the adopted rules of inductive inference shall be "linguistically invariant" under transformations that leave the content of the data about the initial segments of the observed series unchanged. Although he does not argue for this principle explicitly, and holds it to be "trivially" obvious (p. 31), the form in which he states the criterion (p. 30) sufficiently shows what he has in mind. His idea seems to be somewhat as follows: If you turn the premises of your inductive inference into others which *say the same*, you have not changed your data. So, any conclusion you were justified in drawing before you changed the words in which you expressed your data must be maintained *after* the change of language. This is a persuasive idea, but it derives all its appeal from the unnoticed assumption that we are engaged in rational inductive inference. But we have to remind ourselves that we are supposed to be guessing *blindly*, with nothing to sustain us but the hope that if the $l.f.$ exists we shall sooner or later be making guesses close to its value. What matter then if a linguistic transformation requires us to make a different guess, since we know the guesses will be wrong anyway? The reason we guess is not that the guess has any chance of being right (remember Reichenbach's rejection of the possibility of knowing that the estimate is even probable), but merely that persistent guessing may eventually put us on the right track. But this is just as true of the other sequence of guesses that would result from a linguistic transformation of the sort that Salmon discusses. We might almost say that blind posits cannot be in logical conflict, since they cannot even *claim* to be right. To insist that the choice of a blind posit should be unique under linguistic transformation seems to me no more reasonable than it would be to insist that the first trial solution in a process of repeated approximation to the roots of a given equation should be uniquely determined by some rule.

One more specific criticism may be added. Unlike Reichenbach, Salmon takes the $r.f.$ itself, rather than an interval around it, as his estimate of the $l.f.$, and his defense of the "straight rule" depends strongly upon this decision. But it is quite unreasonable to expect the $l.f.$ to coincide with any $r.f.$ If we followed Reichenbach in locating the $l.f.$ within an interval around the $r.f.$ (one whose width, I would suggest, might well be a function of the length of the segment and of the dispersion of attributes in that segment), Salmon's detailed arguments in favor of the "straight rule" would no longer hold. I do not know whether they could be modified so as still to apply.

[Mr. Salmon's reply to Mr. Black is placed at the end of the discussion, since he makes several references to remarks that were made in discussion.]

Discussion on Salmon Paper

(Based on notes taken by TARTAR and BARKER)

WEINER (to BLACK): Does Reichenbach really ignore previous observations when making a new posit?

BLACK: For Reichenbach the new posit is not a simple function of the old; if you shuffled the order of the earlier posits, or lost them, that would not affect the posit you now make. Whereas, in the surveyor's case,[1] each new step depends on the previous one.

SCRIVEN: Perhaps Reichenbach would think that if we can afford to wait for one thousand more observations before making a posit, we might as well do so; but if we do need to make a posit, then we must use all the evidence we have.

BLACK: If we have to make a blind posit under coercion, we might as well choose anything; we might as well say "heads" every time, and not bother to do the arithmetic. There is nothing in the theory at all to guarantee that in the short run fuller observations will give more reliable estimates.

BAR-HILLEL: Reichenbach should have said that the posits are estimates, and not predictions, and hence that they are logical and not empirical statements. But this would be a radical change in Reichenbach's view.

SALMON: Inductive rules in general can be characterized as not truth-preserving. Clearly, the justification of such rules must be different from that appropriate to deductive rules. I should prefer to apply the word "knowledge" to results got by applying the one best inductive rule; Reichenbach's use of the word "knowledge" is bad.

BLACK: I don't believe that it is merely a terminological matter whether the word "knowledge" is to apply here; your proposal is a violent departure from our present use of the word "knowledge," according to which "I know p" entails p. Reichenbach was right, on his principles, to deny that we attain knowledge.

SALMON: If we can show that there is a unique rule having a privileged status, the conclusions obtained by using it should be called "knowledge."

---

[1] Black, in his oral remarks, contrasted the Reichenbach sense of "self-correction" with "self-correction" as it occurs in surveying, where a surveyor will make a rough guess at a quantity; use that guess as the basis for a measurement which may be in error; use the result of that measurement as a basis for a second measurement, which will be more nearly correct than the first measurement; use the result of the second measurement as a basis for a third; and so on.

*   *   *

BLACK: Your formulation of the rule of induction is simpler than Reichenbach's; Reichenbach's rule is that if the observed frequency is f then we should posit that the long-run limit is $f \pm \delta$. The specific vindicatory arguments which you use might not be applicable to Reichenbach's formulation of the rule; δ might be a function of N, and also of the standard deviation. In this case we could get a continuum of rules, to which the vindication of a unique rule would be irrelevant.

* * *

(*The discussion turned again to the question of the validity of the rule of linguistic invariance.*)

BLACK: When you say that "grue things do not look alike," you seem to have an absolute notion of direct resemblance. Yet the Welsh and the Navajo have in their languages different color systems from ours; the Welshman will think that our judgments of what looks alike are arbitrary and wrong. The notion of "looking alike" is relative to our language. Confronted with the same evidence, the Navajo and the English-speaker could use the rule of induction to reach incompatible conclusions.

BAR-HILLEL: This shows that there is no such thing as a rule of induction in Salmon's sense; Popper and Carnap would agree on this. Any rule, in the sense of a principle telling us how to detach conclusions, would lead to contradictions. But who needs such a rule? We can do everything we need to do by computing degrees of confirmation always relative to our data. There is no rule of detachment in inductive logic.

SALMON: It seems to me that science needs rules of induction for the propositions it asserts, even if we do not call them "conclusions."

SELLARS: A principle of detachment is implicit even in Carnap's theory, for presumably there are rules which relate scientific practice to the degree of confirmation of hypotheses. The rule of detachment would concern the conclusion of (scientific) "practical syllogisms." Personally I would make the necessary connection between "degree of confirmation" and a rule of detachment more direct and explicit by construing the very concept of degree of confirmation as a practical (normative) concept.

* * *

SALMON: It is a disturbing feature of Carnapian c-functions that they yield different degrees of confirmation of a given hypothesis relative to given data, in different languages.

NAGEL: I agree. Suppose, for example, that there were two languages spoken by different people, both having the predicates "red" and "square", the second alone having the predicate "soft," the people who speak the first language having no sense of touch. According to Carnap's scheme, the two languages would give different degrees of confirmation to the hypothesis that some unexamined individual is red, given that some n individuals have been examined, and been found to be red.

BAR-HILLEL: What is the matter with saying that one conceptualization works out better than another?

BLACK: It is quite reasonable that degrees of confirmation should be relative to the conceptual framework of the language. An alchemist and a chemist are entitled to measure degrees of confirmation differently relative to the same evidence.

NAGEL: The difference of conceptualization in your example should certainly affect degrees of confirmation, but I don't think this is so in the case of my original example. There are at least some differences in conceptualization that should not affect degrees of confirmation. If we have two intertranslatable languages with different primitives (and different numbers of primitives) one of which contains Huntington's and the other Veblen's axiomatization of geometry, then it would be odd that degrees of confirmation in the two languages should be different.

BAR-HILLEL: Some conceptual frameworks might work better than others; but there need be no rule to tell you which is better.

SELLARS: To evaluate such conceptual frameworks is a task for science. This evaluation is a rational, if complex and messy, process, in which empirical evidence provides good reasons. This is one more reason for insisting that there must be feedback between scientific practice and the choice of a c-function.

BAR-HILLEL: But there can be no rule for this feedback.

*   *   *

SCRIVEN: What does "limit of the relative frequency" mean? Since you cannot demonstrate the existence of a limit, how could you support your claim that this is a meaningful concept?

SALMON: The limit is a mathematical concept being applied within an idealization; we give the standard mathematical definition of a limit. The rule of induction does not define the limit; it is used only to find the limit.

BRAITHWAITE: It would be useful to distinguish between the questions: "Is it a meaningful concept?" and "Does it exist?"

BLACK: We have very strong reason to suppose that the limits do not exist; if I keep tossing a penny, it will be destroyed in the long run, so there is no limit. The concept of the limit of a relative frequency is thus unlike the concept of a perfect gas. If it were a question of an ideal penny, we could have a mathematical theory analogous to pure geometry. But Reichenbach confuses the two levels of idealization, as if they were both somehow on the empirical level.

JEFFREY: Reichenbach, in his *Theory of Probability*, says that talk of infinite sequences is only an idealization, and that what we are really talking about are finite sequences. Reichenbach seems to be trying to back out, where the idealization of the penny is concerned.

SALMON: It would be pleasing if this finitization could be carried out; but even without it, there is analogy enough with the infinite mathematical sequences to provide fruitful application of this notion of the limit of the relative frequency. This notion is like a theoretical term which does not need direct interpretation.

NAGEL: In this respect there is a contrast between Reichenbach's *Philosophy of Space-Time* which emphasizes coordinating definitions for theoretical notions, and the later *Theory of Probability* in which he does not do so. What we need are co-ordinating definitions to give empirical content to the rule of induction.

MADDEN (*after the meeting*): I have certain doubts about the adequacy of Salmon's principle of linguistic invariance for doing the job required of it. Suppose that one of the rules other than the straight one would be successful immediately, but that the straight rule would not be success-ful for two hundred years (which is possible, although, of course, neither known to be true nor known to be false). In these circumstances we would certainly adopt the rule which was successful sooner, saying so much the worse for the principle of linguistic invariance. On the other hand, if we believe that the straight rule is the only really success-ful way of inductively knowing the future, and that such a situation as we envision is impossible, then, of course, we are inductively justifying it and so giving up entirely Reichenbach's vindication. Hence, I believe, the principle of linguistic invariance does not, with complete success, allow us to select the straight rule from all the others which would be vindicated by Reichenbach's vindication.

Reply to Black

by SALMON

According to Professor Black, vindication of induction will seem worth attempting only to those who, like Reichenbach, believe that knowledge of matters of fact is impossible and share his conviction that "the aim of knowing the future is unattainable." When this and similar remarks of Reichenbach are correctly interpreted, it turns out that Black's statement is not unduly restrictive. Reichenbach said, "The aim of knowing the future is unattainable; there is no demonstrative truth informing us about future happenings."[1] This statement denies that predictive statements are necessary and that inductive inferences are demonstrative. Furthermore, when Reichenbach, a frequentist, asserts that the conclusion of an inductive inference cannot be "proved to be probable,"[2] he means that it is impossible to demonstrate that the relative frequency of true conclusions is above any particular fixed value. These views are relatively unexciting and, I think, quite incontrovertible. Reichenbach's usage, which identified knowledge with necessity or certainty, is unfortunate. It would have been far better if he had admitted the possibility of knowledge of the future and had made his views on probability and induction a basis for an analysis of the concept of knowledge of the future, or, more generally, inductive knowledge.

Is inductive knowledge possible? Let us approach the question using the following definition which should prove adequate for our purposes:[3]

S knows p = $_{df}$ (1) S accepts (believes) p,
(2) S has adequate evidence for p, and
(3) p is true.

Suppose we make inductive inferences and accept their conclusions. Do these conclusions represent knowledge? Condition (1) is satisfied by hypothesis. Furthermore, suppose that some of these conclusions are, as a matter of fact, true. For example, suppose we inferred that the sun will rise on September 1, 1961—a conclusion we now know to be true. In this case, condition (3) is also satisfied. The problem hinges on condition (2). Did we have adequate evidence for this conclusion, or is this a case in which we had only true belief but not knowledge? If we maintain that adequate evidence for a conclusion exists only if the conclusion follows deductively,

[1] *The Theory of Probability*, p. 480.
[2] *Ibid.*, p. 475.
[3] Adapted from R. M. Chisholm, *Perceiving*, Ithaca, Cornell University Press, 1957, p. 16.

then, whatever our view of induction, no inductive inference yields knowledge. If, however, we hold that we may have adequate evidence for the conclusion of a correct inductive inference, then some inductive conclusions may constitute knowledge. But what is a correct inductive inference? It is one which conforms to a correct inductive rule. Thus, if some inductive rule can be justified or vindicated, then we can say that inferences which conform to that rule are correct. If the conclusion of such an inference is accepted and if it is, as a matter of fact, true, then all three conditions are satisfied and we may properly be said to have inductive knowledge. Of course, we cannot be certain that a given inference yields knowledge and we cannot be certain that any future inference conforming to this rule will do so. It does not follow that (inductive or nondemonstrative) knowledge of the future is unattainable.

Black's characterization of a blind posit as one "made in total ignorance of any relevant data bearing upon the truth of the posit" seems to me to be incorrect. A posit, blind or otherwise, is a conclusion of an inductive inference. If one holds that relevant data for a conclusion exist only if the conclusion follows deductively from the premises which state these data, then, on any inductive theory, there cannot be relevant data for any inductive conclusion. But if data can be inductively relevant there may be relevant data for blind posits. Data are inductively relevant to a conclusion if it is the conclusion of a correct inductive inference. Whether there are relevant data for a blind posit depends upon whether that posit follows inductively according to a correct inductive rule. When Reichenbach says that the truth-value of a posit is unknown, he is again using the concept of knowledge with certainty or necessity, not inductive knowledge. A blind posit is one that is unappraised, not a wild guess made without relevant data.

If we infer inductively that the sun will rise on a particular morning, we shall find out by observation whether that conclusion is true. If, however, the conclusion is a statement about the value of the limit of a relative frequency, we shall never find out in any comparable sense whether that conclusion is true. We cannot just wait and see, Furthermore, it is well known that any observed frequency in a finite initial section of an infinite sequence is compatible with any value of the limit. Many people have concluded that statements about limits of relative frequencies are unverifiable. To say that any relative frequency in an initial section is compatible with any value of the limit is to say that nothing can be deduced about the limit from a statement of the relative frequency in an initial section. Compatibility is a deductive relation. If verifiability is explicated entirely in terms of deductive relations, then statements about limits of relative frequencies are unverifiable. However, if we admit that there is such a thing as inductive verifiability, then statements about limits of relative frequencies are verifiable if there is a correct inductive rule for inferring their values. The aim of my paper is to show that there is such an inductive rule. If this aim is realized, statements about limits of relative frequencies are verifiable, for they can be conclusions of correct inductive inferences. To deny that there is such a thing as inductive verifiability would be to remove most of science from the realm of the verifiable.

The force of my reply, so far, is to urge examination of my attempt to vindicate an inductive rule. In large part, Black's comments were designed to show that the project was doomed to failure from the beginning. The basic point upon which the reply has rested is that we must take very seriously the fact that we are dealing with problems of induction. When we ask whether inductive inferences yield *knowledge*, whether inductive conclusions are based upon *relevant data*, whether statements about limits of relative frequencies are *verifiable*, we are raising questions about inductive relations. If the concepts of knowledge, relevance, and verifiability are explicated in deductive terms, then we can expect to get negative answers to the foregoing questions. If, however, we admit that these concepts all have important inductive senses, then we cannot answer these questions until we have considered the question of the correctness of inductive rules. If my attempt at vindication is successful, then inductive knowledge *is* possible, inductive conclusions *can* be based upon relevant data, and statements about limits of relative frequencies *are* verifiable. These issues come after an examination of the proposed vindication, not before.

Black's main criticism of my attempted vindication seems to center upon the acceptability of the *criterion of linguistic invariance*. The fundamental justification for this criterion is not that it is intuitively plausible and not that it avoids metaphysics. I believe it has these characteristics and I further believe that the alternative to accepting it is not just metaphysics but outrageous metaphysics. However, the basic reason for accepting the criterion is that it is a consistency requirement. Rules which violate the criterion are rules which lead to formal contradiction. Suppose R is a rule which violates the criterion. There is a consistent set of premises $A_1, \ldots, A_n$ such that:

1. From $A_1, \ldots, A_n$ a conclusion C follows inductively according to R.

2. There is a set of premises $B_1, \ldots, B_m$ which are logically equivalent to $A_1, \ldots, A_n$.

3. From $B_1, \ldots, B_m$ a conclusion C′ follows inductively according to R.

4. C and C′ are logically incompatible.

Using the principle of substitution under logical equivalence we can draw the contradictory conclusion C.C' from the consistent premises $A_1, \ldots, A_n$. An inductive rule which violates the criterion of linguistic invariance sanctions the assertion of a self-contradictory conclusion (and thus, by standard deductive inference, *every* conclusion) on the basis of possible evidence.

If the fact that an inductive rule R leads to contradiction is not sufficient to reject it, an additional point may be made. Anyone who accepts a rule which violates the criterion of linguistic invariance would allow book to be made against him. If his opponent knows what inductive rule is being used, then he may present his bet in one language or another, depending upon what bet he considers more favorable to himself. The person who adopts a linguistically variant rule would accept one or another of different and conflicting bets depending upon the language in which he considers them.

In the discussion at Wesleyan, I was frankly amazed at the equanimity with which some participants were willing to accept such inconsistency as a consequence of Carnap's definition of confirmation in terms of the function c^*. As long as c^* is applied within a single language L, no violation of linguistic invariance can arise.[4] However, there exist pairs of languages L and L' such that use of c^* in both gives rise to interlinguistic contradictions which can be demonstrated in the metalanguage.[5]

Professors Bar-Hillel and Black suggested in discussion that interlinguistic contradictions, unlike intralinguistic ones, are to be expected and tolerated becuase they arise from the adoption of different conceptual schemes. For example, it would be expected that an alchemist and a modern chemist would draw different and perhaps incompatible conclusions from the same observable phenomena. I am quite willing to agree that different conceptual schemes can and should give rise to conflicting conclusions. However, a conceptual scheme is far more than just a language; different conceptual schemes are not merely different notations or different systems of predicates. In such cases as alchemy and modern chemistry at least, conceptual schemes are very general theoretical frameworks. The theoretical frameworks differ with respect to factual content as well as in a purely

[4] R. Carnap, *Logical Foundations of Probability*, Chicago, University of Chicago Press, 1950, p. 316. T59–lh says this, in effect, for all regular c-functions.

[5] This kind of contradiction is discussed in W. Salmon, "Vindication of Induction," in H. Feigl and G. Maxwell, editors, *Current Issues in the Philosophy of Science*, New York, Holt, Rinehart & Winston, 1961. I have shown that there is an extremely strong analogy between this sort of interlinguistic contradiction and the Bertrand paradox for the classical interpretation of probability.

linguistic sense. The alchemist and the modern chemist will draw different conclusions from the same observable phenomena not because they describe these phenomena in different terms but because they accept different and conflicting theories concerning them. We would not regard it as legitimate for a German-speaking chemist and an English-speaking chemist to draw different conclusions from the same phenomena unless, in addition to the linguistic difference, they have relevant theoretical differences. Surely we would not tolerate a bilingual chemist arriving at differing results simply by switching from one language to another.

In my paper I tried to show (pp. 38, 40) that (with suitable restrictions upon the predicates to which it is applied) the rule of induction satisfies the criterion of linguistic invariance. Black and Bar-Hillel challenged this claim in discussion; Bar-Hillel, in particular, asserted unqualifiedly that any inductive rule will lead to contradiction. This objection seems to rest upon the following consideration. Suppose there are two languages L_1 and L_2 with different sets of color predicates; in particular, suppose that L_1 has more color predicates than L_2 so that L_1 permits finer color discrimination than L_2. Let L_1 have the usual color predicates including "blue" and "green," while L_2 has the same predicates except that it has the single disjunctive predicate "blue-or-green" instead of the two separate predicates. Suppose further that a person P_1 who uses L_1 can discriminate between blue and green while a person P_2 who uses L_2 cannot discriminate between blue and green but can discriminate blue-or-green from the other colors. P_1 and P_2 examine the same sample of A's. P_1 sees that all examined A's are blue while P_2 sees that all examined A's are blue-or-green. P_1 concludes that all A's are blue while P_2 concludes that all A's are blue-or-green. P_1 and P_2, it is claimed, arrive at different conclusions from the same evidence, using the rule of induction.

These considerations do not show that the rule of induction violates the criterion of linguistic invariance and they do not show that it leads to any inconsistency. Although P_1 and P_2 have examined the same objects they do not have the same data, for they saw them differently. In any case, *they are not inferring from the same premises* (premises which differ purely linguistically). The premises differ in content; so the conclusions can be expected to also. There is no reason to require that these two inferences have the same conclusions.

I would summarize the situation as follows. *There is one and only one consistent rule* for inductively inferring from the relative frequency of an ostensive property in an initial section of an infinite sequence to the limit of the relative frequency of that property in the whole sequence. This rule is asymptotic. If the relative frequency has a limit, then, for any preassigned degree of accuracy, the inferred value of the limit equals the actual limit within that degree of accuracy for all samples exceeding some finite size. Knowing what we do about the difficulties attending the justification of induction, this seems to be the strongest kind of justification we could hope for.

As Black said in discussion, the enterprise I have undertaken would be quixotic if it had to end at this point. It remains to show how inductive inference can be extended to languages containing non-ostensive predicates and how other types of inductive rules can be vindicated. It seems to me especially important to vindicate a rule for inferring from the limit of the relative frequency to short-run relative frequencies and to introduce more complex rules of inductive inference to deal with the relation between scientific hypotheses and their evidence. In my paper I have tried to provide a basis upon which a more complete inductive theory can be constructed.

III

Induction, Prediction, and Decision-Making in Cybernetic Systems

By W. Ross Ashby

SUMMARY

THE concepts of induction and deduction, as they came to us from the Greeks, were associated with the assumption that they might give a truth that would hold universally without any limit or condition. This assumption, implying that the process ends with an *infinite* quantity of information, is rejected, for no human or mechanical system can process more than a finite quantity.

When the processes of induction and deduction are re-examined in the forms in which they are *actually* used in human thought processes, they are found to follow the same basic methods, and to be subject to the same basic laws, as when they are used in machines.

A NEW START

My first instinct, on approaching the problem of induction, is to go cautiously. The problem is an old one, coming to us from an age that saw the world very differently from the way we see it today. And the way we see it today differs profoundly even from the way it was seen in my adolescence. Before rushing to answer the questions that the Greeks posed, I would prefer today to re-examine the questions, asking whether each question is properly askable.

One aspect at once puts the cyberneticist on the alert. Cybernetics and information theory are alike in being practical, pragmatic, empirical. They think all the time of knowledge as something that is won piece by piece, as something that grows. Statements are not true or false—their probabilities go toward one or zero, but these are the limits, seldom actually achieved. Thus the basic Greek assumption that there are absolute truths, that can be reached in a page or two of logical or mathematical demonstration, leaves the cyberneticist uneasy. He is not used to getting absolute certainty with so little work. I would therefore like to start again from first principles and to see if, perhaps, the Greeks have not unwittingly been misleading us for two millennia.

There comes a time when reconsideration becomes necessary, for however much we may admire the Greeks in some ways, we must admit that they were, in other ways, almost ludicrously ignorant. How long, one wonders, would the average Athenian, alive today, last if he were to start debating with a present-day undergraduate? Sooner or later he would betray that he thought that fire was a substance that came out of wood, or that the winds were blown by big people over the horizon, or that the brain was mucus waiting to come down the nose. We must not delude ourselves into thinking we know everything, but it is a simple fact that a vast amount of knowledge, some of it of profound importance, is available to us today, but was not available to those who first speculated about induction.

The chief reason, of course, for the Greeks' confidence in their philosophy was that they had discovered certain truths which seemed to them to be absolute. Few of us probably have not shared with them the excitement of seeing the demonstration that $\sqrt{2}$ cannot be a fraction, or that the angles inside a triangle add up to two right angles. They felt they had discovered, and demonstrated, that deduction could give absolute truths; so they naturally asked the further question: How may *in*duction lead us to Absolute Truth?

KNOWLEDGE IS FINITE

The cyberneticist, however, is already uneasy. Total certainty, over an *un*bounded universe, is hardly to be obtained except by the reception of an *infinite* quantity of information. The Greek man was no more able to receive an infinitely large quantity of information than modern man is. The communication made in the proof itself—two pages of written characters, say—certainly does not carry an infinite quantity. Are these truths really absolute?

The question is not just philosophic; it has immediate practical consequences, shown at once when we ask: Can a machine find similar truths? To answer this question, let us take an example (equally typical, but more tractable from the machine's point of view). The Greeks discovered that

$$(a + b)^2 = a^2 + 2ab + b^2$$

In particular they knew that the middle coefficient must be a 2. This was typically the sort of truth that they could *prove*.

The computer can, of course, readily compute the two sides for many pairs of numbers, and could readily find that over all its trials no number other than 2 would give equality. If the computer has no better method than that of trial, never reaching absolute certainty, has Man a better method? I suggest he has not.

We know today, of course, that the Greek certainty in this matter (that the coefficient must be a 2) was simply rooted in ignorance. Knowing nothing of vectors, or groups, or matrices, or quaternions, or non-commutative rings, or algebras in general, he picked on one small portion of knowledge and thought it to be universal. Today we know that, far from the equation

$$(a + b)^2 = a^2 + 2ab + b^2$$

being a universal truth, it simply helps to define which of the many possible algebras we are talking about. Thus the statement is true if and only if we wish it to be so.

We can now see that the same is true of the statement that the three angles of a triangle add to 180 degrees. It is true of some spaces, false in others. To insist that it is true is merely to make clear that one must be thinking of a particular class of spaces.

With this view at a distance, we can now see the Greeks' knowledge in its proper size and place. Not realizing that they were unconsciously restricting themselves to a small portion of all knowledge, they thought when they had mastered their portion that they had mastered all there was.

At this point the modern theory of information becomes applicable, for its measures of information always work within a defined and bounded region. If, for example, the region has n cells, or possibilities, and all are equally probable, then one's knowledge is at its *absolute* zero. If information comes, and the probabilities shrink to a single cell, then the gain in information is $\log_2 n$. Here we have gained knowledge that is perfect, or complete, so far as it goes, in the sense that it cannot be increased without our going outside the original assumptions. Yet, in spite of the completeness, the quantity $\log_2 n$ is not infinite. If, however, n, the range of possibilities, becomes infinite, complete knowledge could be obtained only by an infinite quantity of information. Cybernetics is not so unwise as to attempt the impossible. What it does generally is to attempt to obtain knowledge that is complete, so far as it goes, and that requires only a finite amount of information. It recognizes, in the same way, that a finite quantity of information can give completeness only over a restricted domain. It is more modest, and more realistic, then the Greeks; they discoursed of the real numbers, and referred to the "universe" of their discourse. We today talk of a far greater realm of numbers, but we do not call it the *universe* of discourse; we refer to the "region" of discourse. And we know today that whatever is true over a certain region may immediately become false if the region is enlarged.

If I may summarize what I have said so far, the Greeks made a fundamental error in thinking they had discovered truth in any absolute or unconditional sense. In fact, they processed a *finite* quantity of information, which is all that our humanity allows, and they arrived at truths of *finite* range and reliability. It is this finiteness that is the point of this paper. Whether the process is one of induction, deduction, prediction, or decision-making, the quantity of information involved in it is always finite. And this finiteness sets bounds to the possibilities.

INDUCTION

Once we reject the essentially superstitious belief that a mathematician's results are of infinite certainty, the whole theoretical structure of induction, deduction, prediction, and decision-making becomes much easier. For what remains, after the mythical part has been removed, is a perfectly straightforward flow of information, first into the subject during the process of induction, within the subject during deduction, and out from the subject at the decision-making. Let me take them in this order.

Induction, once one has removed the mythical element, becomes simply the collecting of information. What can be said, at any moment, is absolutely bounded by the quantity of information that has been taken in. If one seeks the magic theorem or algorithm that would enable one to say much after receiving little information, then such an algorithm does not exist. Many of the so-called "problems" of induction are nothing more than attempts to deduce more than the data permits; it is not surprising that they are still unsolved. It is to be hoped that as we develop a better intuitive sense of "how much information" we will makes these mistakes less often.

In this connection it must be appreciated that it is only when the facts reach a certain minimal complexity that the concepts of information and induction come into existence. If, for instance, the question were: What can be deduced from the space-traveler's report that he landed on Mars, a white ball appeared on the ground beside him, and then he departed? the answer is: Very little, for the simple reason that such a restricted fact does not permit even the *start* of the concept of information. One is reminded here of how two points on a curve are necessary before the "tangent" becomes definable, three before we can speak of curvature, and four before the concept of torsion becomes meaningful. Attempts to apply the concept of torsion when only three or fewer points exist should not be made. Similarly, the concept of information (and through it of induction) does not exist until a total set of possibilities is properly defined.[1] This criterion will show many of the old so-called problems of induction as merely improper attempts to apply a concept to a set of data inadequate for the concept.

With this point of view, the question of how a person is able to commence the process of induction becomes simply the question of how a system, whether human or mechanical, can receive information. This question has been adequately treated elsewhere and need not be entered into here. The ways that human beings and machines take in information seem to be fundamentally identical. I know of no fact suggesting that there is any fundamental difference.

If it is felt that there must be some sort of special "receptivity" on the part of the system taking in information, I can only say that the evidence is the other way around. It has been shown that if a system is large and has many states of equilibrium (which is equivalent to saying that it is rich in memory), then putting it into an environment that shows law in the transitions it undergoes will result in the system going to a subset of its states such that the subset's transitions resemble (in a certain sense) the pattern of transitions followed by the environment. Thus pattern in the environment inevitably tends to "diffuse" into the system. Only the living brain has been large enough in the past to show the process with

[1] W. Ross Ashby, *An Introduction to Cybernetics*, New York, John Wiley & Sons, 1956.

any clarity but it is of very great generality. An elementary example of it occurs when one stirs a dish of sand with one's fingers; if the finger makes only circular motions one will find afterwards clear marks of circularity in the sand. This example is so well known as to be trivial; what is important is that a similar transfer of pattern can go on in complex mechanisms in which the circularities are complicated and twisted out of all recognition. So in the important case when the world around us shows its properties by its *transitions*, some of its abstract structure will make its way into us whether we like it or not. There is no problem about how to take the information in; it tends to force its way in. This is what "induction" means in cybernetics.

DEDUCTION

The general nature of deduction need not take us long. Once we have disposed of the myth of deduction giving us absolute truths, we can see what is fast becoming recognized by logicians, by mathematicians, and by programmers of computing machines, that "deduction" simply means the carrying through of some well-defined and consistently reproducible process. The emphasis is on the "well-defined." Should the process happen to be isomorphic with some other process, important in itself, then we are pleased. If we find the trajectories of the conic sections isomorphic with those of the planets we are delighted; but the delight is incidental; the deduction requires only that the operations within the conic sections be well defined and not self-contradictory.

From this point of view a digital computer deduces the numerical form of a Bessel function, an analogue computer deduces the flow past an aerofoil, a network of relays deduces the consequences of a set of propositions. Whether a student can deduce the roots of an equation depends simply on whether he can carry through a well-defined process. The *usefulness* of a deduction rests on totally independent criteria, and has nothing whatever to do with the process itself. The work of Newell, Shaw and Simon[2] has made clear that the development of deductive systems of any complexity is only a matter of time and labor. There is no essential mystery about deduction.

[2] A. Newell, J. C. Shaw, and H. A. Simon, *Report on a General Problem-Solving Program*, Internatl. Conf. Inform. Proc., Paris, UNESCO, 1960, pp. 256–64.

PREDICTION

The natural successor to induction and deduction is prediction. Its nature has, I think, been completely clarified by the cybernetic approach. Wiener put his finger on the fundamental axiom when he said that to predict the future is to perform an operation on the past. The essential point is that the agent in the act of prediction depends wholly on the actual past and not in the least on the actual future. When we say of a trained rat that it will not jump through a hole because it *will* receive a shock on the other side, we are guilty of gross confusion of thought and language. We can in fact *demonstrate* that the actual future is quite without effect in this situation, simply by arranging that on this occasion the actual future is to be that the rat is *not* to receive a shock. As everyone knows, the rat's behavior is unchanged. What it is reacting to is its past, which repeatedly contained the sequence

... jump, shock, ... , jump, shock, ... , jump, shock, ...

That living organisms do not react to the actual future, are not affected by it, do not receive information from it, is illustrated vividly when a driver is killed at night by running into an unlit obstacle, or when a soldier steps on a land mine. At ten seconds before the accident he is clearly guided in his actions by what he has seen up to that moment; the fact that he *will* be dead in a few seconds, the *actual* future, has no appreciable effect, though it must be about as powerful a potential stimulus as one can imagine.

That prediction is essentially an operation on the past is also shown very clearly if we reconsider the process of interpolation by Lagrange's method. Here the differences are eliminated, to give a formula in terms of the primary values themselves. Suppose that values, c, b, and a had been observed at times -2 (in the past), -1, and 0 (the present moment). And suppose that we have reason to believe, or are willing to assume, that the quantity is varying on a quadratic law. If we want to interpolate, to estimate the value in the past at

$$t = -\frac{1}{2}.$$

we compute the function

$$-\frac{1}{8}c + \frac{3}{4}b + \frac{3}{8}a.$$

If we compute the function

$$\frac{3}{8}c - \frac{5}{4}b + \frac{15}{8}a$$

(as ordinary a function as the previous one), we are in fact *extra*polating it to give a prediction of what the value will be at

$$t = +\frac{1}{2}.$$

And the function

$$55c - 120b + 66a$$

predicts what it will be at $t = +10$.

The cybernetic view of "prediction" is now clear. It sees nothing peculiar in the process: simply an organism (or an anti-aircraft gun) reacting to its immediate and remote past in the way that every system does. The fact that the gun's mechanics make it point ahead of the plane is a consequence of its design (three years ago) and its input (in the last few seconds). It is the *observer* who, knowing a good deal of what happens under various conditions, describes the events in the most misleading terms of the gun "aiming where the plane will be." Though this way of looking at things is vivid and suggestive, it is basically false and therefore dangerous, especially when one attempts to develop a rigorous theory of behaving systems. The concept of "prediction" is meaningful only when the past shows some constraint, some redundancy. When this is so, the organism, or any reacting system, is able in some way to take advantage of the constraint. Always it uses the past to determine its present action, and the constraint then ensures that the present action shall have a better than chance probability of combining with the events in the real world to achieve the desired goal (Sommerhoff's "focal condition"[3]). The act of prediction thus is simply one of the many ways in which adaptation can show itself. In this sense, prediction can be said to occur in almost every movement we make. I step on this platform, predicting that it will support me. I speak into the microphone, predicting that it will carry my words. The predictions of the astronomer are not essentially different. (The question of the *success* of prediction I will take up in a moment.)

DECISION-MAKING

If the processes of induction, deduction, and prediction are all

[3] G. Sommerhoff, *Analytical Biology*, Oxford, Clarendon Press, 1950.

essentially ordinary—that is, physically realizable—the consideration of decision-making will not detain us long. Machines have no trouble decision making—they just act. Even if an automobile engine refuses to start, the refusal is as much its "decision" of what it is to do as would be a starting-up. Consequently what is usually sought is a "good" or "successful" decision rule.

This is nothing other than the search for an "adapted" form of behavior, viewed from a slightly changed point of view. The formulations of either myself[4] or Sommerhoff help to show the essentials. There must first be a set of disturbances, dangers, threats—from what Sommerhoff calls the coenetic variable—setting up a real problem; and this set must be defined, for the solution depends upon it. There must also be defined the focal condition—what counts as "good," for in general this cannot be taken for granted. The problem then, in Sommerhoff's terms, is to find the decision-rule ρ such that for each situation, *its* output will so combine (by operation ψ) with the other factors τ of the situation that the end result is achievement of the focal condition G. The relation can be stated quite precisely. If the decision rule is ρ, mapping the coenetic values into ρ's output, and if τ is the mapping of the coenetic values into τ's output, and if ψ is the mapping of the just-mentioned couple of outputs into the set of all possible end results, with G the subset of "good" end results, then a necessary property of ρ if it is to be a good decision rule is

$$\rho \subset [\psi^{-1}(G)] \cdot \tau$$

where I use the notation and operations of the Bourbaki theory of sets. If to this we add the requirement that ρ must be a mapping, i.e., everywhere defined (for otherwise the empty set would satisfy the requirement of never issuing a bad decision by refusing to issue *any* decision), we have given the necessary and sufficient condition that ρ should be a good decision rule in the given conditions of τ, ψ, and G.

This relation specifies the decision rule. Certain of its features are worth notice. First, by being stated in general terms, it includes the special cases of the continuous and the linear, but is by no means restricted to them. So it can be applied without the least difficulty to the more general types of material that occur so frequently in biology and in computer processes. Second, it shows just what is essential, in that it depends on:

[4] W. Ross Ashby, *Design for a Brain*, New York, John Wiley & Sons, 2nd ed., 1960.

τ, the environmental factor

G, the defined goal

ψ, the way the rule and the environment interact, and on the domain
of τ, the set of disturbances, eliminated in the composition

And third, it specifies ρ as some member of a class. This is as it should be;
for only in the special cases that are continuous and linear will ρ be
unique.

SELECTION

When the decision rule acts, it performs an act of appropriate selection,
and it at once becomes subject to a rule that has been little used, yet is,
I believe, fundamental in the whole theory of brainlike mechanisms. It
can be most simply stated as a postulate:

*Any system that achieves appropriate selection (to a degree better than
chance) does so as a consequence of information received.*

The postulate is easily defensible on common-sense grounds, for any
system that blatantly violated it would at once be recognized as peculiar.
We are suspicious of the examination candidate who gives the correct
answer before the question has been put, and of the man who fills in an
insurance claim correctly before the fire has broken out! But it can also
be supported more technically; for "selection" and "error correction" are
abstractly identical, and Shannon's tenth theorem[5] shows, under very
general conditions, how the *amount* of appropriate selection is absolutely
bounded by the *quantity* of information supplied.

From this point of view, a "good" decision rule is simply one that
processes *efficiently* the information that comes to it.

The rules for decision will thus always be of the same form. The
possible outcomes are initially many and mixed, good and bad. The set
has to be cut down. The decision rule can only process such information
as is supplied to it. If it is a good rule, it will use the information efficiently
and will thus cut the set down so far as the *quantity* of information permits.
The amount of cutting down is absolutely bounded by the amount of information.
When the information, by its finite quantity, has been used up, no further
selection can be justified. The process has reached its "field of ignorance";
any further selection within this field can only be arbitrary.

[5] C. E. Shannon, and W. Weaver, *The Mathematical Theory of Communication*,
Urbana, University of Illinois Press, 1949.

Here I think we should chose our words with great care, for it is very easy to express the idea in words that are quite wrong—to our own confusion. Thus, one might say, if some selection *has* to be made within the field of ignorance, that "a random choice is as good as any." But this phrase is grossly misleading. By saying a random choice (by spinning a coin, say) *is* as good as any other, one is making a positive statement that can be checked by experiment. What one really means is that when the information is used up, one has no further *justification* for further selection; any further selection must be made arbitrarily.

When the decision rule has used up the information, and has reached the field of ignorance, no further progress has justification. Commonly one then tries to go on by collecting more information. So far as it is collected and used, the process simply remains again subject to the basic postulate. But there often occurs at this point a matter that has been profoundly misunderstood. I refer to the process of "trial and error." This process is of the greatest practical importance but has often been dismissed by the philosopher as trivial. Here it is essential that we appreciate that it has two aspects. On the one hand, it may be a mere grab at success—if it fails, its worth is nothing. Far more important, however, in the general theory of brainlike functioning, is that the process is capable of giving *new information*, the new information by which alone the field of ignorance may be reduced. This latter aspect is seen clearly when one attempts to find one's way out of a maze. When all other information is exhausted, there remains the fundamental method of using trials. Here the success or failure of each trial is not the point; what is important is that as each trial adds further information, the accumulating information allows further and further appropriate selection until eventually the field of ignorance is reduced to the size at which a solution is identified.

There has been some tendency for discussions of brain and computer to be based on the assumption that the computer can use only the method of trial and error, assumed to be futile, while the brain uses some method that is altogether superior. The fact is that when they are similarly situated with regard to the information available, both are equally subject to the postulate. And both may find, at a certain stage in a problem, such as maze-threading, that progress by efficient trial and error is fundamentally the only process possible.

MAN AND MACHINE

The survey I have given suggests that at no point can we find an instance, in the processes of induction, deduction, prediction, and decision-making, where the powers of Man differ essentially from those of an adequately complex and designed mechanism. Both act essentially as processors of information, both require information if they are to work successfully, and both are bounded by the postulate that they cannot achieve appropriate selection in excess of the information available to them.

Do we then jump directly to the simple deduction that Man is a machine? Here again cybernetics cuts right across the old simple ideas; for cybernetics does not admit the question as a proper one. It denies that one can classify the world's systems into, simply, the mechanical and the non-mechanical. *Every* system has mechanistic aspects, so far as it is law-abiding and orderly in its behavior; and there can be little doubt that the human brain does show a good deal of orderliness in its methods even in induction and the others.

Next arises inevitably the question whether Man is more than a machine. I have identified myself for many years with those who have tried to push to the limit the idea that the brain is essentially a form of mechanism, very complex but essentially mechanistic in the sense of being state-determined. The possible inadequacy of the mechanistic aspect has never worried me, for it has always seemed to me to be clear that a demonstration that the brain is more than a machine can be successful only if one first knows thoroughly what one means by a "machine." Only when the idea of machine is pushed to its limit can we see whether the application to Man breaks down or not. Thus those of us who are pushing to the limit the possibilities of what a mechanical brain can do are *defining* the limit to which the machine can go.

One thing seems to me to be clear. The *demonstration* that Man is more than a machine will be done only by him who really knows what the word "machine" means.

Opening Statement

IN view of the fact that Ashby was unable to attend the meeting because of illness, Professor McCulloch and Mr. Verbieck introduced his paper. Professor McCulloch spoke on the background of Ashby's thinking, and Mr. Verbieck underlined some of the points of his paper. The remarks given below are based on the notes of Howard Smokler.

MCCULLOCH: Although Ashby is a professor of electrical engineering, he is primarily a psychiatrist. That means that he has a biologist's attitude. He thinks in terms of an affair in which you locate, by pointing at it, something you call an organism. The rest of the world you divide off as its surroundings. The organism exists only by a continuous give and take. It is open to two things—a flow of energy and a flow of matter—that keep it alive and going. But it has also a second system—a signaling system—that keeps it tied to its world by signals that come from its eyes, its ears, its nose, and so on, which circle through the nervous system and go out over the muscles and glands and whatnot, to alter the input to that system. This is his basic model.

In general, he thinks of an organism as getting signals in, and having got the signals in, it will make a guess as to what the world is like—this is what you can call an induction—it will then perhaps think (and this is perhaps deduction), and it will then make an abduction, a guess as to what the world is like. The guess is embodied in actions which will generate a new set of signals. The organism is undergoing interchange with its environment on two levels: the level of stuff and the level of signals.

VERBIECK: It is on the basis of this notion that he starts his paper with the firm statement that no organism or machine can have absolute certainty about the state of affairs of the world, and he puts this in terms of the impossibility of any organism obtaining an infinite amount of information. On this basis he develops a few simple but basic notions about the induction, deduction, prediction, and decision-making of such mechanisms. Induction is just the process of taking information into the mechanism. Deduction is the carrying through of some well-defined, reproducible processing of the information which has been taken in. The central point in prediction is that the agent, in the act of prediction, depends wholly on the actual past and not in the least on the actual future. For decision-making, he has the same basic notion of a process which is carried out. Making a decision is only possible in so far as the information about the world is not yet exhausted. If we had complete information, we would not need to make decisions. The main point, and the point which Professor Ashby would have emphasized had he been here, is that in all these processes we are concerned primarily with an interaction of the organism and the environment.

Comments on Ashby Paper

By Paul L. Shiman

At the outset I should say that I am in deep sympathy with Ashby's fundamental approach to problems of learning and adaptation, as developed in *An Introduction to Cybernetics* and *Design for a Brain*. Although unfortunately he has not related it to the philosophical literature, his view has the merit of a remarkable philosophical generality—formulating the problems not merely for the scientific enterprise, or for human learning generally, but for all adaptive systems.

But while I see Ashby as riding the philosophical wave of the future, I have a number of problems with that ripple on it which we are discussing. The historical side of the paper I will pass over here. Greek thought will, I trust, survive Ashby's wholesale dismissal without my defense of it. And I will comment only very briefly on Ashby's attempt at a cybernetic account of mathematics and deduction, although it seems to me seriously deficient. For instance, his claim that mathematical statements are true if and only if we wish them to be so may hold for algebras and for geometries, which may be given many interpretations; but for arithmetic, usually understood to have a standard interpretation, this is dubious. Another of his statements is that "Whether the process is one of induction, deduction, prediction, or decision-making, the quantity of information involved in it is always finite." But the Shannon definition of information is not applicable in mathematical contexts; and what is more, it is not clear to me what sort of modification of it would attribute a finite amount of information to concepts like that of the square root of two, or pi, which select one from a non-denumerable infinity of real numbers.

However, the application of information-theoretic notions to inductive contexts raises difficulties more germane to these discussions. Ashby in this paper claims to be working within the framework of Shannon's information theory, in which, as you know, the information conveyed by a received message is determined by the prior probability distribution over the set of alternative messages, according to the entropy formula

$$H = -\sum_{i=1}^{n} \rho_i \log \rho_i.$$

Early in the paper he states, "If the region has n cells, or possibilities, and all are equally probable, then one's knowledge is at its absolute zero." I take it that this means that when all the messages are equiprobable, there is the maximum prior ignorance that can be removed by accurate transmission of the message. Later a similar formulation appears. Shannon's tenth theorem, which formulates the effects of noise on communication, is cited in support of the view that an adaptive organism can only process such information as gets through to it. "When the information, by its finite quantity, has been used up, no further selection can be justified. The process has reached its field of ignorance."

At this point it is important to note that such ignorance, in terms of Shannon's theory, presupposes a good bit of knowledge. In Ashby's field of ignorance, according to Shannon's theory, one is assumed to know the entropy of the source, i.e., the probability distribution over the set of alternative messages. In fact, if the message is totally destroyed by noise, the would-be receiver still has plenty of meta-information with which to make a rational decision. Given his alternative actions and utility assignments to outcomes, he simply maximizes expected utility. From an information-theoretic point of view, Ashby's "absolute ignorance" is far from absolute; it is relative to a body of assumed knowledge.

This illustrates a general point that was made by Black yesterday (if I understood him correctly): that inquiry about induction *always* proceeds against a background of experience about the world; we cannot think ourselves into metaphysical innocence. The results of induction must be used to discuss induction. For instance, Shannon's information measure is defined only for sources that are ergodic; Ashby has to *assume* precisely that limiting characteristic that was argued about so hotly yesterday afternoon.

The difficulty we face in a conference such as this is perhaps that the different languages in which the problem of induction is formulated have different partitions of knowledge and ignorance, and are plausible in different contexts, if at all. However, the proponents of each language claim that induction must be univocally defined in their terms. Someone objected to the use of the term "inductive inference" in Leblanc's paper; we might equally object to Ashby's insistence that induction must be defined information-theoretically.

What is needed, I suggest, is a classification of types of ignorances and information. For instance, such a study might well throw light on disputes concerning the so-called subjective probability viewpoint. The name is extremely unfortunate, suggesting a sharp dichotomy of subjectivity and objectivity, ignorance and knowledge. Luce and Raiffa, in *Games and Decisions*, are perhaps more accurate in classifying subjective probability as decision-making under *partial ignorance*; what Savage provides is a way of processing vague information which cannot be formulated in frequency terms, or even fully captured in the language available. If this is the case, debate might best focus, not on the abstract problem of the definition of probability, but on the concrete task of identifying the contexts in which such a partition is necessary.

One final comment. It is not clear that a cybernetic approach to induction must tie itself to Shannon's concept of information, as Ashby does here. In fact, in his books he uses less restricted concepts. My suspicion is that, when formulated most generally, the cybernetic view will come out as a version of the Peircian view of induction, the inductive validation of inductive policies. Viewed cybernetically, all behavior is regulated by adaptive processes, including the generalized habits of inductive reasoning. Rules of inductive inference are pervasive policies subject to indirect, second-order inductive tests. The reformulation of the Peircian view in cybernetic terms remains a challenging philosophical task for the future.

Discussion on Ashby Paper

(Based on notes taken by HOWARD SMOKLER and PETER CAWS)

SHIMAN: What, precisely, is the relation between cybernetics and physics?

VERBIECK: Cybernetics differs from physics in the same way that biology and circuit theory do; it is interested in systems that look as if they are progressing toward some goal. Thus in cybernetics it makes sense to speak of "good" and "bad," while in physics there is no "good" and "bad": there is just something going on.

MCCULLOCH: In physics things just happen; in engineering devices for transmitting signals, there is information and there is noise. They are both alike physically, but they are not the same from the point of view of utility; this is the cybernetic view.

BAR-HILLEL: I don't think that Mr. Ashby's paper can be taken as representing the cybernetic point of view on induction. In places it is very misleading. He says that "statements are not true or false; their probabilities go toward 1 or 0." There is no conflict here; according to some conceptions statements may both be true or false and have probabilities, relative to other statements, which lie between 0 and 1. The whole notion of information as he uses it is totally undefined. No one, neither Ashby nor anyone else, has given a precise notion of semantic information that is applicable to these contexts; and he is obviously not talking about Shannon's *bits* of information. Even Ashby's statements about deduction are unacceptable, since in no sense in which information has been defined does the conclusion of an argument contain more information than the premises. What we would need for this (and it might be interesting to have it) is some notion of psychological information.

BLACK: I have read some of the technical work on information theory and cybernetics. I have enjoyed it; I have been stimulated; and I think I've learned something. There is no question at all about whether particular theorems are true or whether the applications are correct. This is something in science, and it is judged by scientific criteria. But what we have here is not an instance of science. When Mr. Ashby says that you can't have more information than you get in from the world, he is not making a scientific generalization. He said himself, on the first page, "I would therefore like to start again from first principles." Indeed, if he only knew it, the resemblance between what he is doing and what Aristotle was doing would be enough to shake him.

This is a piece of metaphysics, a certain conception of the world. The difference is that Aristotle was dominated by the idea of an organism with a goal and Ashby is dominated by a conception of a certain sort of machine. If you want to look at human beings as embodied spirits, that is one root metaphor from which a certain kind of metaphysics will emerge. But if you prefer to look at man as a certain kind of machine with input and processing and output, that's another metaphor. And if you think you can make the world interesting and exciting that way, that's fine, but it isn't science. There is an old and respectable name for it, and the name is metaphysics.

Unlike some other people, I really have no objection to metaphysics whatsoever. All I ask is that the people who do metaphysics apply to their work the usual standards of intelligent judgment. What distresses me so much about this and a great deal of other work, which ought to be crossing boundaries and establishing intellectual rapport, is that a man who is a good psychiatrist and a good communications theorist is apt to make such bad mistakes when he starts doing meta-physics. This paper contains demonstrable howlers, such as the idea that induction was something of tremendous interest to the Greeks. When he talks about mathematics, as Mr. Bar-Hillel has pointed out, he also makes serious mistakes.

The real criticism is not that this is metaphysics, because I think that a present-day Aristotle drawing on this new image might really come up with an interesting and exciting view of the world. But I don't think it's going to be done if one simply takes over common-sense ideas of information, confuses them with a technical idea of information, confuses concepts and statements, probability and truth, etc. What's going to result from that is determined (to speak like Mr. Ashby) by the input. The input is muddled and the output will be correspondingly muddled. I hope within the next decade or so that we are going to see the organon of cybernetics. But I don't believe that this takes us even a step in the right direction.

MCCULLOCH: Ashby's trouble is that he is an anti-metaphysician; and every anti-metaphysician I have ever known writes bad metaphysics.

SHIMAN: I think one of the problems is that the philosphers here are saying to themselves, "If only Ashby had been able to take my logic courses or my history courses, he wouldn't have made such mistakes." But of course this is precisely the problem with which this conference was supposed to deal. It is true—and deplorable—that there has been so little communication between the various branches of knowledge represented here.

FINCH: There is a counter-proposal to the proposal that scientists should become sophisticated in logic and philosophy. The only way to break through the crust of restrictive ideas is for scientists to *forget* the history of philosophy.

BLACK: I was not offering a plea for the study of philosophy. I was making only a simple point: that if someone makes a reference to history or to Greek thought, he should take the trouble to get the facts right. And he should also take the trouble to explain words, like "information," which he uses in neither the well-established technical meaning nor in the common-sense meaning, and to state clearly the problem with which he is concerned.

*   *   *

MORGENBESSER (to MCCULLOCH): Can you give us an example of where cybernetics is used to explain or predict something in human behavior?

MCCULLOCH: It was the opinion of Shannon and others that it was impossible to have an information-theoretical "capacity in computation." Working on models of neurons, it has been shown that this is indeed possible.

*   *   *

BRAITHWAITE: I consider Ashby's paper a "prose poem." I enjoyed it very much, but I did not bring my critical powers to bear on it. I suppose if I did, I should find weaknesses. Even regarded in this light it has one shortcoming. It presents an atomistic view of nature—one in which the ultimate elements are *bits* of information. But it shares a shortcoming with other forms of atomism: they generally provide no analysis of the atoms; we never know quite what the atoms are.

IV

The Motivation of Inductive Behavior

By Daniel E. Berlyne

ONE of the distinguishing marks of the kind of psychology known as "learning theory" or, better, "behavior theory" is the belief that the study of intellectual activities should start out from the study of simpler forms of behavior, animal and human. This does not imply a wish to minimize the uniqueness of the human intellect. It is rather a matter of feeling that, since the most sophisticated human capacities must have grown out of humbler functions, we cannot be said to understand either until we have clarified the relations between them. Any principles that may be valid for the whole continuum of behavior will presumably emerge most clearly if we work our way from its lower to its upper pole, as will the nature of the differences that separate the two poles.

There are many questions about induction that fall squarely within the domain of behavior theory as a branch of positive or empirical science and may furnish promising subject-matter for its characteristic research strategy—questions regarding the conditions in which inductive behavior will be launched and the course it will follow.

Yet, traditional discussions of induction have centered largely on normative questions, such as what are the most advisable ways of organizing an inductive process, what are the criteria by which the validity of an inductive conclusion can be determined, and how the legitimacy of induction in general can be defended.

Normative inquiries are nowadays commonly represented as quite different in nature from empirical inquiries. They are, it is contended, concerned exclusively with the question of whether formulae are or are not compatible with the syntactic rules defining a language, so that questions of correspondence and non-correspondence with external reality are outside their competence.

Syntactic rules can undoubtedly be chosen quite arbitrarily, the only limitation being requirements of mutual consistency, and judgments of logical validity can undoubtedly be made without any reference to empirical truth; a conclusion can be deemed legitimate or illegitimate regardless of anything going on in the natural world, just as, according to some views, two and two would still make four even if there were no pairs of objects in the world and nobody to take cognizance of the fact.

Nevertheless, the results of empirical inquiries can be allowed to influence the choice of axioms and rules of inference, and there are ways in which their influence might be helpful. One form of influence arises, of course, when a logico-mathematical system is to be used as a model for a sector of external reality, in which case the choice of properties with which to endow the system must take empirical facts into account. But quite apart from this case, and even when purely normative questions are at issue, there are other reasons why it may be profitable to consider some empirical questions, particularly questions of empirical psychology, before laying down the criteria by which the legitimacy of inductive and other kinds of inference is to be judged.

Induction presumably exists because of some universal characteristics of the interaction between the natural world and the human nervous system, and it has presumably grown up in response to some universal and deep-seated human motives. One can label the inductive processes of practicing scientists "valid" or "invalid" on whatever grounds one wishes. But it would seem that the question of how well these processes satisfy the motives that actuated them in the first place should not be left out of account.

Likewise, the process of discussing the validity of induction has grown out of a somewhat different set of motives which may be at work in scientists during moments when they are not pursuing their occupation— or in quite different individuals, e.g., philosophers. Here again, it would seem advisable to consider why people worry about the justification of induction and what kinds of procedure are best suited to removing these worries, when one is discussing how induction should be justified.

Furthermore, however axioms of rules and inference may be arrived at, questions of validity always turn on questions of consistency. It may seem to be a perfectly objective matter whether axioms and rules that are clearly stated have been followed, or whether they are compatible with one another. But there could be no discussions or conclusions about consistencies or inconsistencies if the human nervous system were not made, for one thing, so that it remembered axioms and rules of inference, and, secondly, so that it recognized and was troubled by later discrepancies from them. And these aspects of our psychology would seem so far to have received less study than they deserve, both on the part of psychologists and on the part of logicians and philosophers who lean so heavily on them.

INDUCTION AS LEARNED SIGNAL BEHAVIOR

From a psychological point of view, induction is a special case of a broad class of behavior that we may call "signal behavior." The defining characteristics of signal behavior are that exposure, on one or more than one occasion, to an ordered pair of stimulus events, (a, b), influences the way in which an organism behaves thereafter in the presence of a, and the influence is such that the organism becomes more likely to behave adaptively in the presence of a.

The stimulus properties may be temporally or spatially ordered, or they may be ordered by categories; e.g., a may be the shape of an object and b its color. And a or b can, of course, be a conjunction of simpler events.

We assume that the performance of a response at a particular time has consequences to which a value, positive or negative, can be assigned. Whether the value is best defined in terms of survival value, hedonic tone, or drive-induction and drive-reduction, is a question that we can leave aside for the moment; these criteria overlap to a large extent but not altogether. The value of the consequences will depend not only on the nature of the response but also on certain external events, which may be called "vital events." We shall say that a response is "adaptive" if the value of its consequences exceeds the expected value of the consequences of a randomly selected response.

One way in which signal behavior can come about is through *natural selection*. If b is an event that gives a positive value to the consequences of a certain response, and if b tends to be accompanied or preceded by a, then organisms that are so made that they perform that response in the presence of a will possess a selective advantage. An association between the response and a is then likely to become part of the unlearned behavior with which a species is endowed.

But in other cases, including most of those that affect the higher animals, signal behavior is a product of *learning*. This means that it results from long-lasting changes in the nervous system, traceable to sensory processes that belong to the life history of the individual in question. And behavior due to induction is an obvious case in point.

There are instructive analogies between the major recognized forms of learning in animals and human induction. But the differences also are instructive.

Let us first consider *instrumental conditioning*, otherwise known as "operant conditioning."[1] An animal performs a response, e.g., depressing a lever, which is closely followed by a reward—a vital event that gives the consequences of the response a positive value. This sequence causes the animal to perform the same response more promptly and more frequently the next time he finds himself in a comparable stimulus situation.

One special kind of instrumental conditioning experiment must receive special mention, since it has sometimes been represented as a prototype of induction. This is the *discrimination-learning* experiment. An animal is confronted with a number of stimulus properties, some of which indicate whether or not a particular kind of behavior will be rewarded, while the remainder do not. Through trial and error, the animal comes to place his behavior under the guidance of the relevant cues and to ignore the others. He may learn, for example, always to approach a certain location if there is a triangle there, irrespective of the color, size, or spatial orientation of the triangle.

The term *"concept formation"* is sometimes applied to discrimination learning in animals. But it is usually reserved for a kind of discrimination-learning experiment which is even more often regarded as representative of human thinking in general and inductive thinking in particular.[2] The subject is exposed to a succession of stimulus patterns with different combinations of attributes. He is informed at the outset that some of these patterns but not others are instances of a certain class, to which, perhaps, a nonsense name is attached. In the course of a training period, he is required to guess which patterns fall within the class, being told immediately afterward whether he has guessed correctly; he is deemed to have completed the learning process when he can invariably distinguish patterns that possess the distinguishing characteristics of the class from others.

But although the conception-formation experiment has provided valuable findings, many of them with an undeniable bearing on inductive

[1] Miller and Konorski (1928), Skinner (1938). See Bibliography, pp. 91–92.
[2] E.g., Bruner, Goodnow, and Austin (1956).

thinking, there are several important respects in which it does not typify thinking, and these limit its usefulness as a research technique.[3]

One is that the concept is chosen arbitrarily by the experimenter; the subject would have no reason to suppose that patterns with a particular attribute or combination of attributes have anything in common to place them apart from others if he were not told so by the experimenter. And he would have no reason to start forming a concept if it were not for the experimenter's urging. In real-life thinking, on the other hand, there must be factors that make the thinker begin his quest spontaneously and factors other than the contingencies contrived by an experimenter to reveal when a new concept of some value has been acquired.

There is however, another point that applies to instrumental conditioning in general, and that is that this kind of learning derives from "subject-dependent" conjunctions of events. Experience of the initial stimulus situation is followed by experience of the reinforcing event, whether it be the appearance of a pellet of food or an indication that a pattern belongs to the class defining a concept, only if the subject executes a particular response.

But, scientific activity is aimed at the establishment of laws referring to subject-independent conjunctions of events. It is true that science enables us to anticipate the consequences of our overt behavior. But even in applied science we identify beneficial courses of action by inference from principles that apply to other phenomena apart from those affected by our behavior. We regard the relations between what we do and what happens because of what we do as derivable from laws with universal and independent validity.

The other principal form of animal learning is *classical* (or Pavlovian) *conditioning*.[4] Here, an indifferent stimulus (the conditioned stimulus) repeatedly precedes an "unconditioned" stimulus, e.g., a puff of air striking the eye, with which a particular response, e.g., blinking, is associated either innately or as a result of previous learning. In consequence of this pairing, the response comes to be evoked by the conditioned stimulus acting alone.

Now, some cases of induction clearly approximate the classical-conditioning pattern. Frequent experience of events a and b in contiguity may well result in the subject learning to respond, on encountering a

[3] Berlyne (1960b).   [4] Pavlov (1927).

alone, with some action that would formerly have been elicited by exposure to b alone. Somebody who has observed that the appearance of nimbostratus clouds is regularly followed by rainfall will probably do some of the things when he sees these clouds that he would do if he saw rain: he might, for example, arrange to have a picnic cancelled, or grasp an umbrella on leaving his house. Verbal responses associated with b are especially likely to occur in the presence of an a that heralds b. But sometimes the adaptive behavior that is carried out in response to a through previous experience of (a, b) is quite different from anything that would be done in the presence of b. A person seeing nimbostratus may rush out to perform an errand that he was going to leave till later, which is precisely what he would not have done if it had been raining.

In cases like the last one, in which *overt* behavior associated with b is not associated with a but nevertheless some behavior occurs that would not have occurred without the prior conjunction of the two events, we may assume that some *internal, implicit* response associated with b has become associated with a and mediates the overt behavior that actually occurs in response to a.

This brings us to a form of animal learning that seems most closely analogous of all to human induction, namely *latent learning*. It has stirred up some heated debates, but it appears to be adequately authenticated in the rat; and, in any case, its existence in cats, dogs, and primates is well established.

In this kind of learning, an animal is exposed to a sequence of stimulus events, subject-dependent or subject-independent, but this exposure does not at the time produce an observable change in behavior. On some later occasion, however, the experience is utilized, and the animal behaves in a manner that shows it to have left some impact on his nervous system. For example,[5] a rat may be given an opportunity to explore a maze without being hungry and with no tangible reward object present. During this period, he samples the various sights and smells that the maze offers and receives them in their fixed order. In a final phase of the experiment, he is allowed to see food in a particular location in the maze while hungry and then immediately removed to the starting box. He thereupon proceeds directly to where the food is, showing that he has benefited from his earlier opportunity to familiarize himself with the layout.

An experiment of this type qualifies as a demonstration of "reasoning"

[5] Seward (1949).

in the rat, since it shows an adaptive response to depend on the piecing together of traces of two different past experiences. This is, of course, a further point that brings latent learning near to human induction, which likewise influences overt behavior through its contribution to reasoning processes.

DETERMINANTS OF THE STRENGTH OF LEARNED BEHAVIOR

At this point, before we go on to discuss some of the peculiarities of inductive learning and its products, we must mention some of the factors that have been found to determine the strength of learned signal behavior.

First of all, we have some factors that are familiar to students of induction. The strength of a learned association generally increases with the *number* of experiences of the conjunction of events that is responsible for the learning, provided that a reinforcing agent (an unconditioned stimulus in the case of classical conditioning and a reward in the case of instrumental conditioning) is present each time. Furthermore, the strength of the learned association increases with the *proportion* of trials on which reinforcement has been present.

Another set of factors has played little part in discussions of inductive logic but receives due recognition in statistical treatments. These concern the phenomenon of *stimulus generalization*; when an association has been brought about between a particular kind of stimulus and a particular response, other stimuli, differing from the original stimulus, will also be found to possess the power of evoking the response without further training. The more similar they are to the original conditioned stimulus, the more generalization there will be. Some of the classical discussions of induction considered the results of drawing a number of red balls out of an urn or of encountering a number of black crows, not considering cases in which the balls that emerged from the urn possessed different degrees of redness and the crows different degrees of blackness. Yet, cases of this sort are extremely important in nature. As Hull (1929) pointed out, we rarely encounter identical conditions repeatedly, and, consequently, a piece of learning would not be of much biological use unless there were a tendency for it to generalize from one stimulus to other stimuli resembling it completely. But in statistical treatments, if we have a random variable that takes on values on which a suitably scaled distance function is defined, we can work out, for example, the most likely shade of coloring of the next ball or the next crow from the central tendency of the colors possessed by previous balls and previous crows.

There is, however, a whole range of other factors that have proved to be of critical importance in animal learning and yet have been almost completely neglected in discussions of induction, where they must be, if anything, even more decisive. These are the factors subsumed under *motivation* and *attention*. How thoroughly an animal will learn something, or whether it will learn it at all, depends on the animal's level of drive and on the nature of the conditions that produced the drive. For example, if an animal is not very hungry, he will not salivate very much at the sight of food, and so a conditioned salivary response, if it occurs at all, will be weak. Similarly, in an instrumental-conditioning situation, an animal that is not very hungry is unlikely to acquire a bar-pressing response that brings about the delivery of food. This is because, for one thing, an animal in a low drive-state is relatively inactive, so that it will not readily hit upon a rewarded response in the course of trial-and-error behavior. Second, if a reward depends on the execution of a consummatory response, such as eating, an animal that is not motivated is unlikely to execute the consummatory response. And third, even if the animal were somehow forced to ingest food when satiated, it is unlikely that this ingestion would function as a reward and reinforce instrumental responses. Similarly, an animal that finds himself in a safe part of a box is highly rewarded if he has been standing a few seconds before on an electrified grid. But freedom from pain will not act as a reward at all for an animal that has not been in pain within the last few minutes.

Furthermore, whether learning will take place at all, and, if so, how effective it will be, depend very much on the nature of the stimuli that are conjoined. In most classical-conditioning experiments, the stimulus to which the response is to be newly attached is paired with a vital event, i.e., one with a beneficial or injurious effect on the tissues. In others, i.e., experiments illustrating so-called "higher-order" conditioning, it is paired with a stimulus that has acquired affective value through previous association with a vital event.

But the properties of the conditioned stimulus also will make a difference. Recent work in Russia[6] has shown that conditioning will be difficult if not impossible to obtain unless the conditioned stimulus evokes, at the start, an "orientation reaction," or in everyday language, unless

[6] Vinogradova (1959).

it "attracts attention." In order to do this, it must have properties like novelty or intensity or complexity or surprisingness to the right degree.

Since, in most naturally occurring situations, an animal is surrounded by many sources of stimulation, all of which may accompany a vital event, the organism's limited information-transmitting capacity makes some selective attention necessary. As some early experiments by Pavlov showed, a combination of conditioned stimuli may be presented and followed by an unconditioned stimulus, and yet, when the elements of the stimulus combination are tested separately, some of them, usually the more intense or striking ones, will be found capable of evoking the conditioned response but others will not have acquired an association with the response at all.

Likewise, an instrumental response may occur and be rewarded in the presence of a whole complex of external stimuli. And of these, some will acquire a strengthened association with the response and some will not be affected. The whole point of discrimination training is, in fact, to restrict control over the response to stimulus characteristics that indicate whether a reward is likely and to eliminate the influence of environmental features that happen incidentally to coincide with the availability of reward on some occasions.

In latent learning, the problem is even more obviously acute. With animals like the rat, latent learning is notorious for its flimsiness and unpredictability. Sometimes, when a rat has had ample opportunity to acquaint himself with facts that could guide him to an adaptive response in a later situation, he seems to have gained nothing whatever from this opportunity. There are plenty of experimental reports on "incidental learning," showing precisely comparable phenomena in human beings. At times, human beings will show remarkable memory for experiences that, when they occurred, had no bearing on any practical concern; and yet, at other times, they will not have retained anything from experiences they have undergone over and over again. Here again, what today appears to be a thwarting capriciousness may turn out to result from our failure to examine the attentive aspects of the problem, to note that exposure to sequences of contiguous stimuli will lead to latent learning only if the stimuli have properties that command attention.

Neurophysiological and psychological work carried out within the last ten years points to much closer connections between problems of motivation and problems of attention than were previously suspected.[7] Russian investigators in particular have favored the conclusion that a stimulus cannot in general play a part in controlling behavior, or become associated with a learned response, unless it alerts the organism or, as they put it, evokes an "orientation reaction." The orientation reaction is a pervasive complex of psycho-physiological processes, mobilizing the sensory apparatus for more efficient absorption of information from the environment and preparing the organism for urgent action. The orientation reaction consists of a momentary rise in the level of "arousal," a variable whose physiology is at present coming under widespread investigation and which appears to be much the same as what psychologists for some time have been calling "drive."

Stimuli that draw attention and alert an animal without being linked with such organic activities as feeding, mating, and escaping from pain are evidently inducing a kind of arousal or drive that prompts behavior leading to the extraction of further information from the same source. In other words, the drive in question is a form of what everyday language would call "curiosity." Discussion of induction have taken surprisingly little account of the obviously true fact that inductive processes will be occasioned by some experienced conjunction of events and not others, that the likelihood and the strength of inductive behavior will vary with the motivational state of the individual in question and with the nature of the stimuli that are coupled with one another.

SYMBOLIC PROCESSES AND KNOWLEDGE

In some instances of signal behavior, including most of the standard classical-conditioning and instrumental-conditioning experiments, the response that the organism has learned to perform in the presence of the signal, a, resembles a response performed at the time of exposure to the conjunction of events, (a, b), that instigated the learning process. But often, as in latent learning, it does not.

When such is the case, we infer that a evokes some internal, implicit process representing b. This representational process may be variously described as an "expectation"[8] or a "mediating response"[9]. It is the behavioristic equivalent of the "thought" or "idea" of b. It presumably

[7] Berlyne (1960a), Lindsley (1957), Morgan (1957).
[8] Tolman (1932).   [9] Osgood (1952).

consists of a curtailed and attenuated version of the neuromuscular and neuroglandular processes that would be occasioned by b if it were present. However conceived, it is an example of a "symbolic process."[10] It is a response, since it is called forth by some stimulus as a consequence of a learning process. But, in its turn, it functions as a stimulus evoking subsequent behavior, including some of the behavior that would be evoked by the event that it represents.

Induction differs from most animal learning and from most simple human learning in that its principal output consists of structures of symbolic processes. These symbolic structures constitute what we call "knowledge."[11] The word "knowledge" is often applied by both philosophers and psychologists to virtually any situation in which an animal responds to, or is affected by, external events. But, since we have other terms like "information" to deal with these more general phenomena, it would seem best to speak of "knowledge" only when there is transmission of information between external events and internal symbolic responses.

EPISTEMIC BEHAVIOR

Organisms do not as a rule remain inactive until the conditions for acquiring a new adaptive response have been fulfilled. Those who think in terms of acquisition of habits stress that animals indulge in trial and error, performing one response after another until they light upon a means of procuring the reward. Those who think in terms of expectations describe animals as trying out one "hypothesis" after another until they have adopted one that is consistently confirmed.

This means that responses that occur before a problem is solved have two functions. Each response is a possible means of reaching the rewarding state of affairs. But whether or not it succeeds in this respect, it is a means of obtaining new information about the consequences of a given way of behaving or about correlations between antecedent and subsequent stimuli.

The relative importance of the reward and the information accruing from a response has been argued over quite vehemently, especially in connection with discrimination learning.

There are, however, some forms of behavior in which the information-gathering function is alone in evidence. These are called *exploratory*

[10] Morris (1946), Osgood (1952), Berlyne (1960a).
[11] Berlyne (1954a).

behavior, when they serve to procure information for immediate use or satisfaction, and *epistemic* behavior, when they serve to procure know-ledge,[12] i.e., information stored in the organism for future use or satis-faction. Exploratory and epistemic responses will, of course, often coincide, since the same behavior can secure information of both short-term and long-term value.

Exploratory behavior includes *orienting* or receptor-adjusting responses, which consist of changes in posture that focus sense organs, and physico-chemical processes within sense organs that enhance their sensitivity. It also includes *locomotor exploration*, consisting of movements toward objects from which information is to be drawn, and *investigatory* responses, usually of a manipulatory nature, forming a residual category. Epistemic behavior, which includes scientific activity, embraces *epistemic observation* (e.g., experimentation), *consultation* of authorities, and *directed thinking*. Directed thinking, which is not only one means of acquiring knowledge but also the principal vehicle by which knowledge acquired by any means is brought to bear on overt behavior, is a special case of reasoning in the sense in which we have already used the term with reference to animal learning.

When we require a response that will perform an information-gathering function without an external-reward-seeking function, a frac-tional form will often suffice. If, for example, we need to know how somebody is going to react to truculent behavior on our part, we do not have to assault him physically; a slightly threatening gesture will in all probability tell us all we need to know. And in thinking, we are able to execute purely internal representatives of overt actions that we might carry out, and we can be led, by these, to an anticipation of the con-sequences that would ensue from them.

We can, in fact, piece together some of the essential features of directed thinking, which is both a vehicle and an outcome of science, if we synthesize some of the ideas that have come from studies of animal learning with some of the ideas that Piaget has derived from his studies of cognitive development in children.[13]

First, a train of directed thinking consists generally of an alternation between symbolic representations of transformations and symbolic repre-sentations of the results of transformations. The representations of trans-formations originate as fractional versions of our own bodily movements,

[12] Berlyne (1960a).   [13] Berlyne (1960b).

and their first function is as substitutes for own actions, enabling us to foresee the effects that these are likely to have. Later, they come to represent logical and mathematical operations or physico-chemical processes that go on independently of anything we may do. But whether we are thinking about the natural world or about a logico-mathematical system, we represent to ourselves an initial situation, then some kind of transformation applied to this initial situation, and finally the new situation that results from the application of the transformation.

The statements that scientific activity yields—whether they take some such form as "Whales are mammals" or as "$d = \frac{1}{2}gt^2$"—establish sequences of symbolic responses with a dual function. For one thing, these statements establish *associative links* between symbolic responses or chains of symbolic responses. Somebody who has ascertained that "whales are mammals" will have learned to say to himself "mammal" in certain circumstances after saying to himself "whale." And somebody who knows that "$d = \frac{1}{2}gt^2$" will in certain circumstances write down "$\frac{1}{2}gt^2$" after writing down "d." Then, these statements establish *behavior equivalences* between the stimulus situations resulting from certain symbolic responses. When we say that two stimulus situations are behaviorally equivalent, we mean that, *given particular motivational states*, they will evoke similar responses. There are, thus, motivational conditions in which the word "whale" and the word "mammal" will be responded to alike, and the same applies to "d" and "$\frac{1}{2}gt^2$."

But the symbolic responses that constitute knowledge are not merely linked together in chains. The chains themselves are organized in systems. Piaget (1936) speaks of "co-ordinations," and what he means seems to be very close to what Hull (1935) called "habit-family hierarchies" A habit-family hierarchy is a collection of chains of responses, all of which start out from the same initial stimulus situation, S_0, and lead to the same goal-situation, S_G. Chains belonging to the same hierarchy can therefore act as alternative means of proceeding from S_0 to S_G.

In the case of knowledge, the chains will be chains of symbolic responses, comprising both representations of transformations and representations of results of transformations. Being chains of internal responses, they will not lead to a common final external stimulus situation, since internal responses do not modify the external environment. But a major consequence of their organization in a habit-family hierarchy will be a behavioral equivalence between the represented situations with which they terminate. Thus, starting out from the same numerical data, we can perform either a series of operations denoted by $(x + y)^2$ or one denoted by $x^2 + 2xy + y^2$, and the end-points of the two series will be recognized as having the same implications for subsequent behavior. Or we could picture ourselves moving five miles to the southeast and then eight miles to the north or moving three miles to the east and then four miles to the north, and we realize that, whichever itinerary we followed, we could return to our starting point from wherever it left us by moving five miles to the southwest.

One final point about knowledge structures is that, since they are not restricted to representation of real contingencies, they make it possible to think of sets of alternative but mutually exclusive possibilities and consider them in relation to one another. Piaget's studies[14] show how indispensable this is for the kinds of thinking that make logic, mathematics, and science possible and, according to his findings, make their appearance in early adolescence. The sixteen relations between two propositions, p and q, that are recognized by the proposition calculus correspond to the elements of the power set of $\{(p \cdot q), (\bar{p} \cdot q), (p \cdot \bar{q}), (\bar{p} \cdot \bar{q})\}$. And in order to verify, for example, that p implies q, a subject must be able to represent to himself the four possibilities, $(p \cdot q)$, $(\bar{p} \cdot q)$, $(\bar{p} \cdot \bar{q})$, and $(p \cdot \bar{q})$, and then to ascertain that instances of the first three exist but the fourth is not realized. Likewise, in order to conduct a valid experiment showing which factors exert a causal influence on a certain physical or chemical phenomenon, one must be able to devise a procedure in which possible causes are enumerated and then tested in turn with the others held constant (or varying orthogonally to it), perhaps later trying out all possible combinations of the factors in case there may be interaction effects.

These points have a bearing on the psychological origin of probability judgments. Situations to which we apply the concepts of probability theory are usually ones whose outcomes we are not able to control precisely, either because, as in tossing a coin, control of the outcome would require more precision of force and direction than our motor processes could muster, or because the outcome depends on so many and, perhaps, such small-scale processes acting independently and simultaneously that we could not operate on them all at once.[15] Consequently, representational processes deriving from overt actions are not able to conduct us

[14] Inhelder and Piaget (1956).
[15] Mowrer (1960), ch. 8; Piaget (1953), ch. 6.

to an exact representation of the outcome. Subjective probabilities, in the sense of habits or expectations of varying strength, exist in quite small children and in lower animals. But an understanding of laws of objective probability does not come until the ages of eleven or twelve, as Piaget's investigations show.[16] Children after that age can understand that, if a box containing a row of red beads and a row of white beads is shaken up, a disorderly pattern will result and the original separation of red and white beads is unlikely to recur. This, Piaget says, is because, once they can conceive of the various patterns that could result from the shaking up, they appreciate that disorderly ones are numerous, while the original orderly pattern is unique.

THE MOTIVATION OF EPISTEMIC BEHAVIOR

The motivational problems that must be raised in connection with induction are those that pertain to epistemic behavior in general and correspond to those that have arisen in the course of studying simple forms of learning. They bear on the factors that determine when inductive behavior will begin, how long and how vigorously it will be pursued, to what sectors of the natural world it will be directed, when it will terminate as successfully completed, and when it will be abandoned as not worth pursuing further.

Epistemic behavior will often be actuated by familiar sources of drive such as may underlie other behavior, e.g., internal physiological disturbances, like hunger, thirst, and sexual appetite, and noxious external stimuli. They also include the states of fear or anger induced, through learning, by stimuli, internal and external, verbal, or non-verbal, that have been contiguous with such biologically threatening states of affairs. When epistemic behavior is aimed at the acquisition of knowledge that will serve the practical aims of removing these conditions, we may speak of it as "extrinsic epistemic behavior."

But there are times when knowledge is pursued apparently for the sake of "truth," with no practical application in view. When this happens, we speak of "intrinsic epistemic behavior," and we must seek further afield for its motivational antecedents.

The kind of drive state that instigates and steers intrinsic epistemic behavior may best be called "epistemic curiosity" to distinguish it from

[16] Piaget and Inhelder (1951).

the "perceptual curiosity" that motivates some varieties of exploratory behavior, although they must have a great deal in common. Both are apparently induced by stimulus patterns that are strange, puzzling, ambiguous, unclear, surprising. All these terms refer to conditions in which conflict, i.e., the simultaneous arousal of incompatible forms of behavior, can be expected. And a quite impressive number of different lines of psychological research[17] has in recent years been converging on the conclusion that the states of discomfort, or "drive," or "high arousal's that make organisms restless and foment new learning can arise not only out of visceral disturbances and external irritations but also from disharmonies among an organism's own reactions.

The type of conflict that gives rise to epistemic curiosity will be conflict between symbolic-response-tendencies—beliefs, attitudes, thoughts.[18] And the attributes of knowledge structures that we have already reviewed reveal several ways in which such conceptual conflict could come about.

Since knowledge entails expectations, stimulus patterns might very well materialize that clash with them. Such cases of *surprise* or *incongruity* must generate conflict between a reaction determined by the actual nature of the stimulus pattern that occurs and reactions held in readiness for the pattern that was expected. There can be latent *inconsistencies* that make themselves felt and provoke distress when an external stimulus pattern draws discrepant reactions from two different symbolic structures.

Since, as we have seen, the ability to contemplate a set of alternative possibilities is such a prominent feature of symbolic behavior, we shall frequently have the kind of situation to which the information-theoretic measure, *uncertainty* (entropy), is applicable. And this measure will have a high value when the number of contemplated alternatives is large and when their probabilities approach equality.

The recent movement to discuss inductive and similar processes in terms of decision theory advocates that we pay attention to the practical consequences that may follow from espousal of, or action on, a belief. This gives due recognition to the necessity of considering motivational factors. But so far, only extrinsic motivational factors have received attention, which has led some writers to protest against this mercenary view of the quest for knowledge, and to point out that knowledge is so often sought and found satisfying for its own sake.

[17] Berlyne (1960a).   [18] Berlyne (1954a), (1954b), (1962).

In the language of information theory, there can be no receipt of information if there is no initial uncertainty, since, if information-theoretic concepts are to applicable, an event must be one of a set of anticipated alternatives, each with its associated probability-value. And psychologically also, we can suppose that knowledge can have no intrinsic reward-value without some initial conceptual conflict giving rise to epistemic curiosity.

The concept of uncertainty, in the sense used by information theory, and the concept of conflict are very close.[19] If we consider the conditions that should be fulfilled by a measure of "degree of conflict," we can see that "uncertainty" fulfills most of them, so that, all things being equal, conflict should be more severe the greater the uncertainty. But information theory deals with probabilities, i.e., relative strengths of responses, which precludes it from covering all the factors relevant to conflict. Degree of conflict must depend not only on uncertainty, i.e., the distribution of probabilities, but also on the absolute strengths of the competing processes —on how thoroughly the responses have been learned, on what gains and losses are at stake, on how strongly entrenched are the beliefs that are being questioned.

Once a conceptual conflict has been induced, there are many ways in which it can be diminished, including running away from the stimulus pattern that precipitated it, ceasing to entertain thoughts that are troublesome or puzzling, or simply contorting beliefs into a more comfortable mold. But in many cases the only way in which conceptual conflict can be permanently relieved, as distinct from temporarily alleviated, is by securing additional information, and hence new knowledge, through epistemic behavior. New knowledge may relieve conflict by strengthening one response and weakening its competitors, or by modifying knowledge structures to remove inconsistencies and inaccuracies, thus reducing the likelihood of future encounters with external stimulus situations that jar with them. A satisfying conclusion to a quest for knowledge means not only abatement of existing conceptual conflict, but also insurance against conceptual conflict in the future.

Most of those who have hitherto considered scientific activity and the logical and psychological processes related to it have begun at a point where the inquirer already has a problem. In psychological experiments,

[19] Berlyne (1957); (1960a), ch. 2.

the experimenter usually imposes a problem on the subject and, not infrequently, he also decides arbitraily when the problem is solved. And specialists in inductive thinking generally assume that the thinker already has an interest in studying a class of phenomena.

If, however, we look at the work of the great thinkers of the past, whether in science, logic, mathematics, philosophy, or even art, we can see how their originality and ingenuity so often lay in the kinds of questions they asked and in the ways in which their questions were framed. Once a question has been formulated, the rest is often not so difficult. And any question means a choice among myriads of possible objects of inquiry that surround one at every moment. If these motivational aspects of induction and cognate activities receive more investigation, they may well turn out to have a bearing on some of the problems that have been debated for centuries.

Bibliography

Berlyne, D. E. (1954a), "Knowledge and Stimulus-Response Psychology." *Psychol. Rev.*, 61, 245–54.

Berlyne, D. E. (1954b), "A Theory of Human Curiosity." *Brit. J. Psychol.*, 45, 180–91.

Berlyne, D. E. (1957), "Uncertainty and Conflict: a Point of Contact between Information-Theory and Behavior-Theory Concepts." *Psychol. Rev.*, 64, 329–39.

Berlyne, D. E. (1960a), *Conflict arousal and curiosity*. New York, McGraw Hill.

Berlyne, D. E. (1960b), "Les équivalences psychologiques et les notions quantitatives." In Berlyne, D. E. and Piaget, J. (1960), *Théorie du comportement et opèrations*. (Etudes d'Epistémologie Génétique, vol. XII), Presses Universitaires de France, Paris.

Berlyne, D. E. (1962), "Uncertainty and Epistemic Curiosity." *Brit. J. Psychol.* 53, 27–34.

Bruner, J. S., Goodnow, J. J., and Austin, G. A. (1956), *A Study of Thinking*. New York, Wiley.

Hull, C. L. (1929), "A Functional Interpretation of the Conditioned Reflex." *Psychol. Rev.*, 36, 498–511.

Hull, C. L. (1934), "The Concept of the Habit-Family Hierarchy and Maze Learning." *Psychol. Rev.*, 41, 33–52; 134–52.

Inhelder, B., and Piaget, J. (1956), *De la logique de l'enfant à la logique de l'adolescent*. Presses Universitaires de France, Paris. (*The Growth of Logical Thinking from Childhood to Adolescence*. New York, Basic Books, 1958).

Lindsley, D. B. (1957), Psychophysiology and Perception. In *The Description and Analysis of Behavior*. Pittsburgh, University of Pittsburgh Press.

Morgan, C. T. (1957), Physiological Mechanisms of Motivation. In M. R. Jones (ed.), *Nebraska Symposium on Motivation* 1957. Lincoln, University of Nebraska Press.

Mowrer, O.H. (1960), *Learning Theory and the Symbolic Processes*. New York, Wiley.

Miller, S., and Konorski, J. (1928), Sur une forme particulière des réflexes conditionnels. *C.R. Soc. Biol.* 99, 1155–57.

Osgood, C. E. (1952), "The Nature and Measurement of Meaning." *Psychol. Bull.*, 49, 197–237.

Pavlov, I. P. (1927), *Conditioned Reflexes*. Oxford, Clarendon Press.

Piaget, J. (1936), *La naissance de l'intelligence chez l'enfant*. Neuchâtel and Paris, Delachaux et Niestlé. (*The origins of intelligence in children*. New York, International Universities Press, 1952).

Piaget, J. (1953), *Introduction à l'epistémologie génétique. II. La Pensée Physique*. Paris, Presses Universitaires de France.

Piaget, J., and Inhelder, B. (1951), *La genèse de l'idée du hasard chez l'enfant*. Paris, Presses Universitaires de France.

Seward, J. P. (1949), "An Experimental Analysis of Latent Learning." *J. Exp. Psychol.* 1949, 39, 177–86.

Skinner, B. F. (1938), *The Behavior of Organisms*. New York, Appleton-Century.

Tolman, E. C. (1932), *Purposive Behavior in Animals and Men*. New York, Appleton-Century Crofts.

Vinogradova, O. S. (1959), "The role of the orientation reflex in the process of forming conditioned connection in man." in Sokolov, E. N., *Orientirovochny refleks i voprosy vys'shei nervnoi deiatel'nosti* (*The orientation reflex and questions of higher nervous activity*.) Moscow: Acad. Pedag. Sci.

Opening Statement

By BERLYNE

THE discussion of induction is in itself an interesting psychological phenomenon. It is clear, as the response to Ashby's paper has shown, that it is a highly professionalized activity, so that it is hard, if not dangerous, for an outsider to offer a contribution to it. Nevertheless, it is worth while to ask how this activity originated and attained its present form. According to one view, the "bloody-minded" view, any axiom system is acceptable as long as it fulfills the usual requirements of consistency, independence, and completeness, and nobody has the right to ask where its originator got it from. On the other hand, philosophers of science are wont to criticize axiom systems on the ground that they are "counter-intuitive" or that they do not reflect the way in which scientists actually work. Whether such criticisms are valid or not is clearly an empirical question within the domain of the behavioral sciences, but the informality with which they are customarily handled contrasts sharply with the rigor that philosophers demand for other parts of their inquiry. Closer contact between philosophers and behavioral scientists might therefore be profitable.

As a second point, there is a current tendency to slur over the differences between inductive behavior in human beings and somewhat analogous phenomena in parts of the animate and even inanimate worlds. This tendency is partly inspired by a desire to avoid vitalism and mentalism, but the differences between human induction and anything found elsewhere in the animal kingdom are too important to be ignored and could be handled in a naturalistic way.

There are important psychological problems concerning what has occurred before the point at which philosophers usually take up the problem of induction. Philosophical discussion generally begins with a man who, for some reason, is anxious to know whether the balls in a certain urn are all white or whether all crows are black. But it is surely impossible to understand induction, whether in everyday life or in scientific activity, without asking such questions as in what conditions somebody will concern himself with an urn or with crows rather than with the multitude of other phenomena that people the universe, why he should be so eager to know whether they are all white or all black as the case may be, and how he got the idea that they might all be of the same color in the first place.

Comments on Berlyne Paper

By William Kessen

T HE character of this company and Professor Berlyne's first name put me almost inevitably in mind of the Biblical tale and, although I have not yet clearly discerned who is the King of Babylon and who are the lions, I have no doubt about who is in the pit. Because of the imbalance here between philosophers and psychologists, I will tend in my remarks to join Daniel in the den rather than taking advantage of the commentator's opportunity to engage in the play available to lions. Speaking more seriously, and assuming that I have heard correctly the discussions of the last two days, I am unsure whether you believe that a psychologist has anything of significance to say about the problem of induction. However, cheered by the fact that psychology may be the only discipline that shares with philosophy the possibility of being both trivial and wrong, I will speak to several points in Professor Berlyne's paper and then add an observation or two in the hope of finding directions toward a meeting place for psychologist and philosopher of induction.

First, I am unsure about the boundaries to put on the term "induction" or, to make Professor Berlyne's not inconsequential change, "inductive behavior." I am convinced that it includes more than the drawing of inferences about the contents of hypothetical bags and urns, but I wonder whether the notion of inductive behavior should be broad enough to include the behavior of rats in a discrimination-learning apparatus. In order to establish a field of choice, let us consider the following cases, addressing to each the question, "Is this properly called inductive behavior?"

1. A white rat, trained to run a straight alley in at least five seconds, when place in the starting-box one day after one hundred trials, runs the alley in 5.1 seconds.

2. A human infant cries. As his mother walks towards his crib, he stops crying.

3. A college sophomore is confronted with a complicated concept-formation task (for example, a disjunctive concept modeled on exclusive alternation in logic). He is correct—that is, his answers conform to the experimenter's view of the concept—85 per cent of the time. When asked to state the rule under which he is answering, he does so in a way that, were he truly using such a rule, would give him only 50 per cent successes in the conventional sense.

4. A case corollary to the one given just above is of the subject who states the correct answer on every occasion *and* states correctly the rule which governed the construction of instances of the concept.

5. Another college sophomore is presented with a randomly ordered series of red cards and black cards such that in the entire pack there are 70 per cent red cards and 30 per cent black. He is asked to guess the color of each card just before it is exposed. His guesses, after a few hundred presentations, turn out to be pretty close to 70 per cent "Red" and 30 per cent "Black."

6. And, in the case of apparent induction based on considerations other than the evaluation of the physical environment (a case which has not been addressed at all in these meetings), a businessman in late 1960 considers the evidence available, calls on his best inductive apparatus, and votes the straight Republican ticket.

These cases, and the variety could easily be greater, represent different problems for the psychologist and I am curious whether they represent different problems for the philosopher of induction. I do in this regard seem to disagree with Professor Berlyne in that I would prefer to consider inductive behavior to include only those cases where an explicit statement is made by the inducer. Action theories or action inductions, whether the rat's, the child's, or mine as I drive my car knowing nothing of automotive mechanics or the physiology of muscles, do not seem happily called inductions. If the field of application is narrowed so as to include only the making of explicit statements, then the psychologist can look to those circumstances or conditions of the utterance of sentences of a certain kind, typically general statements about the natural environment.

The only other point where Professor Berlyne and I may not be inseparably allied concerns the theoretical matrix from which he draws his discussion. The stimulus-response-reinforcement position seems to be committed to the analysis of topographical behavior, that is, to an exclusive dependence on the learning of movements that can be described geographically or anatomically. All else is presumably stimulus (or response of stimulus-response) generalization. My respect for the founders and continuers of this tradition and my desire for simplicity of formulation make me wish it were so, but it seems more reasonable to believe that human beings oftentimes (though by no means always) learn rules or categories rather than movements. To say that someone learns to add does not seem perfectly equivalent to saying that he had learned certain topographical responses—for example, to say "six" in the presence of the stimulus "What are four and two?"—and has generalized these responses.

The most impressive human example I know is the child's learning of natural grammar. He learns pluralization rules, rules of word order, rules of intonation, rules for appropriate use of parts of speech all of which seem to go beyond what we presently know about the learning of topographical responses. The example that Professor Berlyne cites in his paper about mammals and whales (p. 86) would, under a strict interpretation of his theory, lead to the statement that the person in question also knew that mammals are whales.

Let me hurry to add two footnotes. I have no positive alternative theoretical program for dealing with the learning of rules or categories. However, such learning appears relevant to any psychological account of inductive behavior, and our technical equipment is presently inadequate. Second footnote: I am not proposing an abandonment of associationistic analysis of these problems and a return to some modulated a priorism. The point here is again that we may require sharper theoretical tools to build our explanatory house.

This realignment with Professor Berlyne and his empiricism permits me to go on to underline several points that he made in his paper. First, I do not believe that either of us would like to propose that you turn the problem of induction into a psychologistic search for the Laws of Thought, but I for one am concerned with the absence of boundary conditions for the occurrence of induction. Is this a point too obvious to be made aloud or is the problem of inductive inference to be phrased purely as the discovery or invention of a unique technique to extract a general statement from a series of events? To speak baldly, I am looking for *variety* in the paths between a collection of occurrences and a summary sentence. Let me say why I want variety or at least the statement of which idealized inducer we take as our model. Take the case of the deck of cards, 70 per cent red and 30 per cent black. On exposure to repeated instances, you remember that the typical sophomore will match his guesses to the pack. A three-year-old on the other hand will, under certain circumstances, guess some favored color until it comes up—if I may speak for the three-year-old, he will make it be black. The four- or five-year-old shows another pattern. Having learned (and you will see again how elaborated our notions of learning must be) that alternation is a good strategy, he will alternate "Red" and "Black" resistively. Finally, a game theorist faced with this inductive problem will very quickly start naming "Red" all the time in order to maximize (he maintains rationally) his successes. The point is obvious—presented with the same physical events, in the same order, in roughly the same social context, four different kinds or states of induction-makers draw strikingly different conclusions. As I remarked earlier, I am not sure if all of these are "true" inductive behaviors, but the problem posed is general—information does not fall on homogeneous and unfiltering human tissue. The state of the *tabula* at the moment of writing, from *rasa* to *plena*, determines the character of inductive behavior, a conclusion demonstrated in detail and with great ingenuity by Jean Piaget.

One last remark. Professor Berlyne has outlined very neatly indeed the motivating occasions for inductive search or inductive behavior, and I strongly second his emphasis on conflict and discrepancy as central. He had space to touch only briefly on the other side of inductive behavior— what stops it. In many ways this is the most fascinating of the psychological problems, and unless I misread it may be one of the crucial philosophical problems. When do you quit the inductive search? What is the occasion for termination? When is the problem solved? Under what circumstances does one say, "O.K., I have seen enough; I will now declare myself or take action"? My hunch is that by the time the scientist, say, commits himself to an explicit statement he has tried out several candidates for his statement and rejected or modified them by test operations of various kinds. The philosophical problem of induction, to judge by the examples used in these meetings, is the evaluation of an "old" induction—one that the scientist is willing to expose to criticism or, in Professor Braithwaite's proposal, to propose as an answer to an examination question.

Let me close with a complex summary, and consciously provoking wish. It would comfort my black psychological heart to be able to say (1) that the problem of induction is the problem of specifying the occasions on which explicit statements about nature are made, the evaluation of these statements, and the taking of action in the light of this evaluation; (2) that the invention or development of these statements (or hypotheses) is, contrary to the traditions of philosophy, a psychological, sociological, anthropological, or other empirical problem and not in the domain of the philosopher except as he functions as theoretical psychologist, sociologist, or anthropologist; (3) that the evaluation of these statements, once made, may conceivably be regularized and reconstructed along the lines discussed here this week; and (4) that the study of the taking of action is again in the domain of the empirical scientist, though here I am far less certain of the dimensions of investigation. On this last count, the notion of betting odds may be a seesaw with room for both philosopher and psychologist. The question implicit in Professor Berlyne's paper I will ask more bluntly: Psychologists have a great technical engine, not perfectly functioning but in some ways useful; is there any way we may fruitfully use it on the problem of induction?

Discussion on Berlyne Paper

(Based on notes taken by PETER CAWS and HOWARD SMOKLER)

MORGENBESSER: I wonder if Mr. Berlyne would say a little more about the theory of symbolic behavior: is it an alternative to stimulus-response theory, or an outgrowth of it?

BERLYNE: When I spoke about symbolic behavior, I considered it as a form of stimulus-response theory. It all turns on whether you can define symbolic responses behavioristically. The whole thing was started by a philosopher, Charles Morris ...

MORGENBESSER: But there have been very serious criticisms made of Morris's approach.

BERLYNE: I'm not aware of any very valid criticisms of Morris's approach, aside from details. I don't see anything wrong with the approach on *a priori* grounds, and on *a posteriori* grounds, this approach has been extremely productive of both theoretical and experimental work. There is an unfortunate tendency in non-psychological circles to impute a "nothing but" to Morris's approach. But it is not to be conceived as an attempt to say all that can be said about thinking; it is an attempt to deal with certain aspects of symbolic processes.

*   *   *

BAR-HILLEL: It is difficult when professionals of various fields meet together to know whether they are talking about the same problem from different points of view, or whether differences of opinion are due to the fact that they are perhaps talking about two different problems. Psychologists deal with concept formation and theory formation; they even deal with inductive behavior. But I wonder if they are dealing with the same problem that philosophers are dealing with. Even the game theorist described in Mr. Kessen's comments (p. 96) has not reached the problematic stage of induction. It is when we want to know if the next card will be red, or if the proportion of red cards will remain .3, that we become involved in the philosophical problems concerning induction.

BERLYNE: It is said that people do things better when they know just what they are doing and why; so perhaps, if this is so, philosophers who want to talk about induction might do well to examine their own behavior and ask why they and other people are doing this. And if you take this problem in its general form, of *understanding* induction, we are all interested in understanding induction. And understanding, whatever else it may involve, also involves the empirical discussion of what people induce, how they induce, why they induce, and so on.

KYBURG: I think that what Ernest Nagel said at the first session may be relevant. He said there were two kinds of problems: (1) the articulation of the rules of inductive behavior; and (2) the justification of these rules. One way of articulating the rules is to look at the way people actually make inductions; another way might be to make them up out of whole cloth. There's no limitation on where you get the rules from. And philosophers are in just as good a position as anyone else (but no better, perhaps) when it comes to making up rules. The other thing, the justification of these rules, seems on the other hand to be a definitely philosophical problem. And I'm not sure, even after reading Professor Berlyne's paper, that psychologists are even interested in contributing in this particular respect.

WEINER: The relation of psychology to logic is an old problem; the usual answer to the request for a connection is that logic gives justification.

BERLYNE: It's an open question what people mean by "justification." There seems to be an implicit feeling on the part of philosophers that if you could see induction justified you'd recognize it. There are various ways in which you can approach the problem of justification, however, and this is only one of them. You can also approach the problem in empirical terms.

BLACK: You *can* approach the problem in empirical terms. You can ask, for example, why philosophers are concerned with the problem, and trace their concern to some neurosis or compulsion. But philosophers of induction think that there is a rational core to the problem of induction, i.e., that there is a *rational* answer to the question, "Why is one inductive procedure better than another?" Philosophers ask for *good* reasons. The philosophical problem is whether (1) there are good reasons; (2) there are no good reasons; or (3) that the very request for good reasons is unreasonable. Empirical procedures have their relevance. They do not serve to provide good reasons. But giving good reasons involves setting up models, and empirical evidence can help to free the imagination in setting up such models. There still remains the normative-descriptive distinction.

BERLYNE: Who is to judge what is a good reason and what is a bad one?

BLACK: We are; adult, intelligent, English-speaking persons.

CAWS: In one respect the function of science seems to be to cut off an area to philosophical discussion, as in Ashby's claim that where there is no uncertainty an organism cannot make choices.

BLACK: I think that particular point is a logical one. But of course it is true that philosophers pay attention to empirical facts. Philosophers do not wish to say what is not true, and to listen to what scientists have to say helps them to avoid this.

*   *   *

MORGENBESSER: I would like to raise a question as to the relevance of psychological evidence to inductive philosophy. In experiments on concept-formation, psychologists often do not really ask how people form concepts, but only examine whether their way of forming concepts is like that of the experimenting psychologist.

BERLYNE: There are better experiments and worse experiments; the kind of experiment you describe would certainly not be relevant to the philosophical problem of induction.

MCCULLOCH: (to BLACK) Tell me now, what would a philosophically minded logician regard as a satisfactory solution to the problem of induction?

BLACK: There is no simple answer to that. Just as in the case of mathematics one would have to look at actual mathematical practice to discover the standard of mathematical proof, so one would have to look at philosophical practice in this case. Philosophical training consists exactly of learning to recognize when the answers to philosophical questions meet certain requirements and when they do not.

V

A New Approach to a Classical Statistical Decision Problem

By Herbert Robbins

This research was supported by the Office of Naval Research under Contract Number Nonr–266(59), Project Number 042-205. Reproduction in whole or in part is permitted for any purpose of the United States Government.

I

INTRODUCTION

W E shall present a new way of looking at the old problem of testing a simple statistical hypothesis against a simple alternative *when the problem is assumed to occur not once but repeatedly*. The result (expressed by Theorem 2 below) seems interesting both from the point of view of the foundations of statistical inference and for its usefulness in practical situations.

We assume that the "state of nature" in a hypothesis-testing problem is represented by a parameter θ which can take on only two possible values denoted by o (the "null hypothesis") and 1 (the "alternative"); and that as usual there are only two possible actions A_0 ("acceptance") and A_1 ("rejection") open to the experimenter, such that A_0 is appropriate when $\theta = o$ and A_1 when $\theta = 1$. If the experimenter takes action A_0 when in fact $\theta = 1$, we assume that he incurs a loss of a units due to incorrect decision; while if $\theta = o$ and he takes action A_1, he incurs a loss of b units. Finally, we assume that, although the true value of θ is unknown, the experimenter can observe the value of a random quantity x whose *probability distribution* P_θ depends on θ. The question is, how should the experimenter use the observed value of x to decide which action to take, in such a way as to minimize in some sense the expected loss due to incorrect decision?

A (randomized) *decision function* t is a function $o \leq t(x) \leq 1$ which is such that when x is observed the experimenter will take action A_1 with probability $t(x)$ and A_0 with probability $1 - t(x)$, the randomization being done with the help of a table of random numbers or some such device. (If $t(x)$ is restricted to the two values 0 and 1 it is said to be non-randomized; in this case the value $t(x) = 1$ means "take action A_1" and $t(x) = 0$ means "take action A_0.") In using t, the expected loss due to incorrect decision is given by

$$(1) \qquad \begin{cases} R(t; 0) = bE_0(t(x)) & \text{when } \theta = 0 \\ R(t; 1) = a[1 - E_1(t(x))] & \text{when } \theta = 1, \end{cases}$$

where E_θ denotes expectation with respect to the probability distribution P_θ.

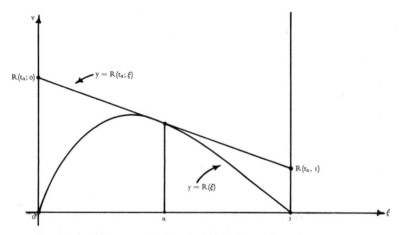

Figure 1. The Envelope Risk Function $R(\xi)$

A good decision function t is one which gives low values to both "risks" $R(t; 0)$ and $R(t; 1)$. Since, however, a low value of one of these can in general only be obtained by allowing a high value for the other, it is of interest to consider weighted averages of the two risks, defined for any constant $0 \leq \xi \leq 1$ by

$$(2) \qquad R(t; \xi) = \xi R(t; 1) + (1 - \xi)R(t; 0),$$

and to ask for the decision function t which minimizes (2) for some fixed ξ. Denoting any t which minimizes (2) by t_ξ (we shall see in a moment how to compute t_ξ), we then have for any $0 \leq \xi \leq 1$ and any t,

$$(3) \qquad R(t_\xi; \xi) \leq R(t; \xi);$$

and for any $0 \leq a \leq 1$ and $0 \leq \xi \leq 1$,

(4) $$R(t_a; \xi) = \xi R(t_a; 1) + (1 - \xi)R(t_a; 0).$$

The *envelope risk function* $R(\xi)$ defined by

(5) $$R(\xi) = R(t_\xi; \xi) = \min_t R(t; \xi),$$

is fundamental to what follows.

To compute the decision functions t_ξ for any $0 \leq \xi \leq 1$ we may assume without loss of generality that the two probability distributions P_0, P_1 are given in terms of their density functions with respect to some measure μ on the x-space; thus

$$E_\theta(t(x)) = \int t(x)f(x, \theta)d\mu \qquad (\theta = 0, 1),$$

and hence from (1) and (2),

(6) $$R(t; \xi) = \xi a + \int [(1 - \xi)bf(x, 0) - \xi af(x, 1)] \cdot t(x)d\mu.$$

It follows that for fixed ξ, $R(t; \xi)$ is minimized by the function

(7) $$t_\xi(x) = \begin{cases} 1 & \text{if } (1 - \xi)bf(x, 0) < \xi af(x, 1) \\ 0 & \text{if} \qquad ,, \qquad > \qquad ,, \\ \text{arbitrary} & \text{if} \qquad ,, \qquad = \qquad ,, \end{cases}$$

In minimizing $R(t; \xi)$ we can resolve the ambiguity in (7) by choosing the non-randomized decision function

(8) $$t_\xi^0(x) = \begin{cases} 1 & \text{if } (1 - \xi)bf(x, 0) < \xi af(x, 1) \\ 0 & \text{otherwise} \end{cases}$$

The minimal value of $R(t; \xi)$ is, by (6) and (8),

(9) $$R(\xi) = R(t_\xi; \xi) = \xi a - \int [(1 - \xi)bf(x, 0) - \xi af(x, 1)]^- d\mu,$$

where by $[x]^-$ we mean $-x$ if $x < 0$ and 0 if $x \geq 0$.

Concerning the function $R(\xi)$ we remark that for any $0 \leq a \leq 1$ the straight line in the ξ, y-plane (see Figure 1)

(10) $$y = R(t_a; \xi) = \xi R(t_a; 1) + (1 - \xi)R(t_a; 0)$$

passes through the point $(a, R(a))$ of the curve $y = R(\xi)$, and that since $R(\xi) \leq R(t_a; \xi)$ the curve lies by (3) everywhere below the straight line. The curve $y = R(\xi)$ is therefore concave and hence continuous, and passes through the two points $(0, 0)$, $(1, 0)$.

We are now in a position to give a meaningful interpretation to the weighted average $R(t; \xi)$ of the two risks $R(t; 0)$, $R(t; 1)$ associated with any decision function t. In fact, if the parameter θ is itself a *random variable* with a priori probabilities

(11) $\xi = P[\theta = 1], \; 1 - \xi = P[\theta = 0],$

then $R(t; \xi)$ represents the "global" expected loss due to incorrect decision when we use the decision function t. Hence, if ξ is known, the "Bayesian" solution of the decision problem is simply to use the t_ξ defined by (8), since this affords the minimum value $R(\xi)$ of $R(t; \xi)$.

There are, however, two questions involved here: (1) Does ξ exist; i.e., does it make sense to regard θ as a random quantity? and (2) Assuming ξ exists, how do we know its value? The first question depends in part for its answer on our interpretation of the word "random"; as to the second, it must be admitted that we shall often be quite ignorant of the true value of ξ, despite any dogmatic rules which may be adduced in support of one value or another. We shall not discuss these questions here. Instead, we hall present another interpretation of $R(t; \xi)$, *formally* similar to the, Bayesian one, but *conceptually* quite distinct.

II

THE COMPOUND DECISION PROBLEM

Suppose we are faced with a *sequence* of decision problems of the same normal structure as before. Thus let

(12) $\begin{cases} \theta_1, \theta_2, \dots, \theta_n; \text{ each } \theta_i = 0 \text{ or } 1 \\ x_1, x_2, \dots, x_n \end{cases}$

be a finite sequence of parameter values and observable random variable each x_i associated with θ_i in such a way that the probability distribution of x_i is P_{θ_i}, independent of all the other θ's and x's. Suppose we must sake one of the actions A_0 or A_1 for each θ_i, $i = 1, \dots, n$. If we use the *same* decision function t throughout, so that we take action A_1 in the ith problem with probability $t(x_i)$, then the expected loss on the ith decision will be $R(t; \theta_i)$ and the *average expected loss on the set of n decisions* will be

(13) $\dfrac{1}{n} \sum_{i=1}^{n} R(t; \theta_i) = \bar{\theta}_n \cdot R(t; 1) + (1 - \bar{\theta}_n) \cdot R(t; 0) = R(t; \bar{\theta}_n),$

where we have set

(14) $\bar{\theta}_n = \dfrac{1}{n} \sum_{i=1}^{n} \theta_i = \text{proportion of } 1\text{'s among } \theta_1, \dots, \theta_n.$

Thus $R(t; \xi)$ can also be interpreted in a non-Bayesian sense as simply the average expected loss in any finite sequence of decisions in which the proportion of times that $\theta = 1$ is ξ. And hence, if we have n decisions to make and know the value of θ_n, we can achieve the value $R(\theta_n)$ for our average expected loss by using $t\bar{\theta}_n$ throughout.

Of course, we shall in general not know in advance either n or θ_n. However, in some cases we shall be in the following position: *at the time when the i*th *decision is to be made, we shall know the values of* $\theta_1, \theta_2, \ldots, \theta_{i-1}$ as well as that of x_i. This suggests the following procedure, call it T: for the ith decision use the decision function $t^0_{\theta_{i-1}}$ defined by (8); i.e., take action A_1 if

$$(15) \qquad (1 - \bar{\theta}_{i-1})bf(x_i, 0) < \bar{\theta}_{i-1} \, af(x_i, 1),$$

and otherwise take action A_0. (For i $= 1$ we may set $\bar{\theta}_0 = \frac{1}{2}$.) A possible motivation for this is simply that at the ith stage of our sequence of problems, the value $\bar{\theta}_{i-1}$ is our best available estimate of θ_n. We now state our first theorem:

THEOREM I

Assume that $f(x, 0)$ and $f(x, 1)$ are such that $R'(\xi)$ exists and is continuous for all $0 \leq \xi \leq 1$. Then given any $\epsilon > 0$, there exists an integer $N(\epsilon)$ such that for any $n \geq N(\epsilon)$,

$$(16) \qquad R(T; \theta_1, \ldots, \theta_n) \leq R(\theta_n) + \epsilon,$$

uniformly for all sequences $\theta_1, \ldots, \theta_n$, where by $R(T; \theta_1, \ldots, \theta_n)$ we mean the average expected loss in using the decision procedure T,

$$(17) \qquad R(T; \theta_1, \ldots, \theta_n) = \frac{1}{n} \sum_{i=1}^{n} R(t\bar{\theta}_{i-1}; \theta_i).$$

Thus if n is large we can do almost as well with T as if we knew at the outset the values of n and θ_n and used the decision function $t\bar{\theta}_n$ throughout the n decisions.

PROOF OF THEOREM I

First we have the easily verified relation

$$(18) \qquad \frac{1}{n} \sum_{i=1}^{n} R(t\bar{\theta}_i; \theta_i) - R(\theta_n) = \frac{1}{n} \sum_{i=1}^{n-1} i[R(t\bar{\theta}_i; \theta_i) - R(t\bar{\theta}_{i+1}; \theta_i)].$$

and since each of the terms in the sum on the right is ≤ 0 by (3), it follows that

$$(19) \qquad \frac{1}{n} \sum_{i=1}^{n} R(t_{\theta_i}; \theta_i) \leq R(\bar{\theta}_n).$$

Next, we observe that by the assumed continuity of the derivative of $R(\xi)$ it is easily seen from Figure 1 that $R(t_a; 0)$ and $R(t_a; 1)$ vary continuously with a. Hence for every $\epsilon > 0$ there exists a $\delta = \delta(\epsilon) > 0$ such that for $0 \leq \xi, \xi' \leq 1$,

$$(20) \qquad |\xi - \xi'| < \delta \text{ implies } \max_{\theta = 0, 1} |R(t_\xi; \theta) - R(t_{\xi'}; \theta)| < \epsilon.$$

Finally, we remark that

$$(21) \qquad |\bar{\theta} - \bar{\theta}_{i-1}| \leq \frac{1}{i}, \qquad (i = 0, 1, \dots, n)$$

irrespective of the values of $\theta_1, \dots, \theta_n$; $\theta_i = 0, 1$.

Now to prove the theorem. Let $\epsilon > 0$ be given. Choose δ by (20) so that $1/\delta$ is an integer and

$$(22) \qquad |\xi - \xi'| < \delta \text{ implies } \max_{\theta = 0, 1} |R(t_\xi; \theta) - R(t_{\xi'}; \theta)| < \frac{\epsilon}{2}.$$

Then if $N(\epsilon) \geq \dfrac{2M}{\delta\epsilon}$, where we have set $M = \max(a, b)$, it follows that for any $n \geq N(\epsilon)$,

$$\frac{1}{n} \sum_{i=1}^{n} R(t_{\bar{\theta}_{i-1}}; \theta_i) \leq \frac{1}{n} \sum_{i=1}^{n} R(t_{\bar{\theta}_i}; \theta_i) + \frac{1}{n} \sum_{i=1}^{n} |R(t_{\bar{\theta}_i}; \theta_i) - R(t_{\bar{\theta}_{i-1}}; \theta_i)|$$

$$\leq R(\bar{\theta}_n) + \frac{1}{n} \sum_{i=1}^{1/\delta} |R(t_{\bar{\theta}_i}; \theta_i) - R(t_{\bar{\theta}_{i-1}}; \theta_i)|$$

$$+ \frac{1}{n} \sum_{i=1/\delta+1}^{n} |R(t_{\bar{\theta}_i}; \theta_i) - R(t_{\bar{\theta}_{i-1}}; \theta_i)|$$

$$\leq R(\bar{\theta}_n) + \frac{M}{n\delta} + \frac{\epsilon}{2} \leq R(\bar{\theta}_n) + \epsilon,$$

which was to be proved.

The trouble with T is of course that the values $\theta_1, \dots, \theta_{i-1}$ must be known at the time of the ith decision. *We shall now remove this restriction.*

THEOREM 2

Assume that $f(x, 0)$ and $f(x, 1)$ are such that $R'(\xi)$ exists and is continuous for all $0 \le \xi \le 1$. Then there is a decision procedure T^* with the following property: given any $\epsilon > 0$ there exists an integer $N(\epsilon)$ such that for any $n \ge N(\epsilon)$,

$$(23) \qquad R(T^*; \theta_1, \ldots, \theta_n) \le R(\bar{\theta}_n) + \epsilon,$$

uniformly for all sequences $\theta_1, \ldots, \theta_n$, where by $R(T^*; \theta_1, \ldots, \theta_n)$ we mean the average expected loss in using T^*, *and where at the ith decision we assume known (and use) only the values*

$$(24) \qquad x_1, \ldots, x_i.$$

DISCUSSION OF THEOREM 2

The idea in defining T^* is, in contrast to T, to use at the ith decision the decision function $t^0_{p_{i-1}}$, where $p_{i-1} = p_{i-1}(x_1, \ldots, x_{i-1})$ is an *estimate* of θ_{i-1} based on $x_1, \ldots, x_{i-1}$. This may be done as follows.

Choose some set S such that $P_0(S) \ne P_1(S)$, and let

$$(25) \qquad g(x) = \begin{cases} 1 & \text{if } x \in S, \\ 0 & \text{if } x \notin S. \end{cases}$$

Define

$$h(x) = \frac{g(x) - P_0(S)}{P_1(S) - P_0(S)};$$

then $h(x)$ is bounded and is an unbiased estimate of θ, i.e.,

$$(26) \qquad E_\theta(h(x)) = \theta; \theta = 0, 1.$$

Let

$$(27) \qquad \psi(x_1, \ldots, x_i) = \frac{1}{i} \sum_{j=1}^{i} h(x_j);$$

then no matter what the values of $\theta_1, \ldots, \theta_i$ we have

$$(28) \qquad \begin{aligned} E(\psi(x_1, \ldots, x_i)) &= \bar{\theta}_i, \\ \text{Var}(\psi(x_1, \ldots, x_i)) &\le \frac{C}{i}, \end{aligned}$$

where C is some finite constant. Finally, let

$$(29) \qquad p_i(x_1, \ldots, x_i) = \begin{cases} \psi(x_1, \ldots, x_i) & \text{if } 0 \leq \psi \leq 1, \\ 0 & \text{if } \psi < 0, \\ 1 & \text{if } \psi > 1, \end{cases}$$

and set $p_0 = \frac{1}{2}$. Then for large i, p_i is a reliable estimator of θ_1. Hence it is reasonable, in view of Theorem 1, to investigate the properties of the decision function T* which requires that we take action A_1 at the ith decision if and only if [cf. (15)]

$$(30) \qquad (1 - p_{i-1})bf(x_i, 0) < p_{i-1}af(x_i, 1).$$

It is not difficult to show that T* actually has the property (23) stated in Theorem 2. The detailed proof will be given in the forthcoming doctoral dissertation of Miss Ester Samuel.

We have assumed in Theorem 2 that $R'(\xi)$ exists and is continuous. Even when this is not the case, as for example when x has discrete distributions P_0 and P_1, Miss Samuel has shown that there exist *randomized* versions of T* which satisfy (23).

This is the first publication of Theorem 2, but for previous work in the same direction the reader may consult the Bibliography at the end of this paper, items 1 and 3.

III

CONCLUDING REMARKS

In Figure 2 we have sketched the risk functions in the compound decision problem for three statisticians, A, B, and C, for the case in which $R'(\xi)$ is continuous.

1. A uses T*, and if n is large his average expected loss will be approximately $R(\xi)$, where in the sequence of n parameters $\theta_1, \ldots, \theta_n$ the proportion of 1's is ξ.

2. B is a Bayesian, and thinks that in the sequence of n decisions, $\theta_1, \theta_2, \ldots, \theta_n$ are independent random variables with $P[\theta_i = 1] = a$, $P[\theta_i = 0] = 1 - a$. He therefore uses the decision function t_a throughout. If in fact the true proportion of 1's among the n values $\theta_1, \ldots, \theta_n$ is ξ, his average expected loss will be $R(t_a; \xi)$, which may be much larger than $R(\xi)$.

3. C adheres to the minimax school, and uses a decision function of the class (7), call it t_{ξ_0}, throughout, chosen so as to make

$$(31) \qquad R(t_{\xi_0}; 0) = R(t_{\xi_0}; 1) = R(\xi_0) = \max_{\xi} R(\xi).$$

It follows that no matter what the values of $\theta_1, \ldots, \theta_n$, C's average expected loss will be $R(\xi_0)$, which may still be considerably higher than $R(\xi)$.

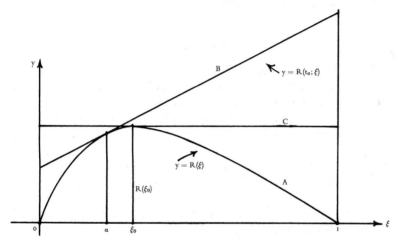

Figure 2. Comparison of risks

It would seem that unless there are strong grounds for believing that we do in fact know the quantity ξ quite accurately, it will be preferable to follow A's example and use T*. Of course there is a great deal to be said pro and con on this subject, but the object of this paper is to provoke rather than to exhaust the philosophical and practical discussion of the compound approach versus the more conventional alternatives. We do not put forward T* as by any means "optimal" (in fact, it is not even "admissible" in the sense of Wald), and it is clear that there are modifications of T* which would make it much more reasonable in most practical situations. The important point is that when a statistical decision problem is looked at from the compound point of view, so that the ith decision is based on $x_1, \ldots x_i$ rather than x_i alone, there is available a much wider class of decision procedures within which to seek a solution with desirable properties. The relation to stochastic learning and adaptation theory is obvious.

It is hoped in future papers to explore further decision problems, e.g., composite hypothesis testing, estimation, etc., from the compound approach, and to prove asymptotic distribution and convergence theorems for the average loss as $n \to \infty$.

Closely related to the "compound" approach of the present paper is the "empirical Bayes" approach of the Bibliography, 2 and 4. Together, they would seem to point to an exciting future development of a somewhat moribund domain of classical statistical inference.

Bibliography

1. H. Robbins, "Asymptotically Subminimax Solutions of Compound Statistical Decision Problems." *Proceedings of the Second Berkeley Symposium on Mathematical Statistics and Probability*, 1950.
2. H. Robbins, "An Empirical Bayes Approach to Statistics." *Proceedings of the Third Berkeley Symposium on Mathematical Statistics and Probability*, 1955.
3. H. Robbins and J. F. Hannan, "Asymptotic Solutions of the Compound Decision Problem." *Annals of Mathematical Statistics*, Vol. 26, 1955.
4. M. V. Johns, Jr., "Non-parametric Empirical Bayes Procedures." *Annals of Mathematical Statistics*, Vol. 28, 1957.

Discussion on Robbins Paper

(Based on notes taken by PETER CAWS)

BRAITHWAITE (in lieu of official commentator): If I understand the import of Mr. Robbins paper, then this is an historic occasion; it seems to me the most significant advance in statistical decision theory since the development of Wald's minimax method.

The theorem developed in this paper reminds me of a result in game theory conjectured by G. W. Brown,[1] and established by Julia Robinson.[2] They consider a sequence of "fictitious plays" of a two-person zero-sum finite game, the sequence being determined by the recursive rule that in the k'th play, each player has to use the pure strategy best for him against the *average* of the (k − 1) pure strategies used by his opponent in the previous (k − 1) plays. (In the first play each player might use any strategy.) In other words, in each play a player has to act on the assumption that his opponent will use the mixed strategy which is equivalent to the average of the strategies he has used in the past. Robinson proved that, in a sequence of plays determined in this way, for each player the sequence of these mixed strategies—i.e., the averages of the pure strategies used by him in the preceding (k − 1) plays—will converge as k increases without limit, to the optimal strategy for the game, and the average gain for the maximizing player will converge to the "value" of the game.[3] As Brown said, this iterative method "can be loosely characterized by the fact that it rests on the traditional statistician's philosophy of basing future decisions on the relevant past history. Visualize two statisticians, perhaps ignorant of minimax theory, playing many plays of the same discrete zero-sum game. One might naturally expect a statistician to keep track of the opponent's past plays and, in the absence of a more sophisticated calculation, perhaps to choose at each play the optimal pure strategy against the mixture represented by all the opponent's past plays."[4]

---

[1] "Iterative solutions of Games by Fictitious Play," in *Activity and Analysis of Production and Allocation*, T. C. Koopmans, editor, 1951.

[2] *Annals of Mathematics*, Vol. 54, 1951.

[3] The Brown-Robinson iterative method is described and illustrated in J. C. C. McKinsey's *Introduction to the Theory of Games*, 1952, and in J. D. Williams' *The Compleat Strategyst*, 1954, p. 182.

[4] *Loc. cit.*

ROBBINS: The analogy between the game-theoretical situation and my theorem doesn't seem exact; the Brown-Robinson case supposes that both players are playing, while my method is indifferent to the behavior of one player, i.e., Nature, and concerns itself solely with the strategy of the other.

BRAITHWAITE: If the method works when Nature is playing deliberately against the statistician, a fortiori it will work when Nature is assumed not to be an active player.[5]

*   *   *

KYBURG: Is the antecedent condition that the sequence of decisions should consist of identical cases realistic? In other words, do sequences to which this method is applicable ever actually occur, and if they do occur, how do we know when a given sequence is one of them? In what sense does the method yield "better results"? Can one be sure—or even expect—that there will be an improvement as instances accumulate?

ROBBINS: Any individual case or partial sequence of cases might come out badly on the use of the method; the method controls only the *average* expected loss. As to the identical nature of the problems dealt with, while in principle (as long as the distribution of the x's on the θ's remained the same) one could use the results from one science to throw light on problems from another, in practice the easiest cases to handle, of which there are many, involve repetitions of the same test. For example, consider the decision whether or not to release batches of a certain vaccine, on the basis of tests on guinea pigs. The state $\theta = 0$ is here taken to mean that the virus is alive, the state $\theta = 1$ that it is dead. x is the state of the guinea-pig; $x = 1$ if $\theta = 1$, where $x = 1$ signifies that the guinea pig lives, $x = 0$ that it dies. If $\theta = 0$ there is a known chance P that the guinea pig will die. In this case we have $P(\theta = 1) = \xi$, $P(x = 0) = 1 - \xi$, where ξ is unknown but assumed small. Now the technique used by some laboratories is to release vaccine that tests "good," on the assumption that the a priori probability of "bad" is so low as to make the risk negligible in any particular case. But by my method the accumulation of apparently independent bad tests would lead to the revision of this a priori estimate.

[5] Subsequent to the conference, Mr. Braithwaite wrote as follows: "I realize that my reply was invalid: the Brown–Robinson iterative method is only applicable to zero-sum games, where there is direct opposition between the interests of the players; and cannot be extended to more general games. So there is very little in the analogy I pointed out."

LEVI: Do we have to know that the distribution of the x's given the θ's remains the same in the diverse cases?

ROBBINS: Yes.

BLACK: This paper illustrates a principle in which I strongly believe, namely, that experience modifies not only the method of approach to particular cases, but also the methodology itself. The fundamental problem of induction remains, however, that of justifying the adoption of a method even when everybody agrees that it is the right one.

ROBBINS: Mistakes in selecting a method carry a penalty, even in a game; and in real life such mistakes can lead to the elimination of those who adopt the wrong strategy.

VI

Temporally Asymmetric Principles, Parity Between Explanation and Prediction, and Mechanism versus Teleology

By Adolf Grünbaum

I am indebted to Professor Allen I. Janis for helpful discussion of aspects of statistical mechanics relevant to section II. The treatment of the barometer as an advance indicator in section II benefited from a criticism which Mr. Nicholas LaPara made of an earlier formulation.

After completing this paper, I became aware that some of the objections to the Popper-Hempel thesis which are criticized in my section III were also discussed independently by Professor May Brodbeck in her essay "Explanation, Prediction and 'Imperfect Knowledge,'" which is published in H. Feigl and G. Maxwell, editors, *Minnesota Studies in the Philosophy of Science*, volume 3. Unfortunately, it was too late to make specific mention of Professor Brodbeck's contributions within the text.

I

INTRODUCTION

IN order to consider the role of temporal asymmetries in scientific induction, I wish to deal with three major questions. These are:

1. What are the principles governing those conditions under which there is the following kind of temporal asymmetry of inferability: It is possible to infer from the state of a system at some particular time t_0 one or more states at times t *prior* to t_0—this inference being called a "retrodiction"—but the same information pertaining to the time t_0 does not permit the corresponding predictive inference concerning the times $t > t_0$?

2. What is the bearing of the existence of the asymmetry between retrodiction and prediction on the following quite distinct question: Is

there symmetry between the *explanation* of an event E on the basis of one or more *antecedents* of E, when E belongs to the *past* of the explaining scientist, on the one hand, and, on the other hand, the *prediction* of the same (kind of) E by reference to the same (kind of) *antecedent(s)* of E, when E belongs to the *future* of the scientist making the prediction?

3. What is the import of our findings in regard to the two preceding issues for the controversy between mechanism and teleology?

II

CONDITIONS OF ASYMMETRY BETWEEN RETRODICTIONS AND PREDICTIONS

Our concern in this section is with the kind of asymmetry in which retrodiction is possible while the corresponding prediction is impossible.[1] To deal with it, we must first give an account of certain features of the physical world having the character of initial or boundary conditions within the framework of the theory of statistical mechanics. The sought-after basis of the asymmetry will then emerge from principles of statistical mechanics relevant to these *de facto* conditions.

The universe around us exhibits striking disequilibria of temperature and other inhomogeneities. In fact, we live in virtue of the nuclear conversion of the sun's reserves of hydrogen into helium, which issues in our reception of solar radiation. As the sun dissipates its reserves of hydrogen via the emission of solar radiation, it may heat a terrestrial rock embedded in snow during the daytime. At night, the rock is no longer exposed to the sun but is left with a considerably higher temperature than the snow surrounding it. Hence, at night, the *warm* rock and the *cold* snow form a quasi-isolated subsystem of either our galactic or solar system. And the relatively low entropy of that subsystem is purchased at the expense of the dissipation of the sun's reserves of hydrogen. Hence, *if* there is some quasi-closed system comprising the sun and the earth, the branching off of our subsystem from this wider system in a state of low entropy at sunset involves an entropy increase in the wider system. During the night, the heat of the rock melts the snow, and thus the entropy of the rock–snow system increases. The next morning at sunrise, the rock–snow subsystem

---

[1] For a discussion of the conditions under which the *inverse* asymmetry obtains, see A. Grünbaum, "Das Zeitproblem," *Archiv für Philosophie*, vol. 7, 1957, pp. 184–85. Cf. also M. S. Watanabe, "Symmetry of Physical Laws. Part III. Prediction and Retrodiction," *Reviews of Modern Physics*, vol. 27, 1955, pp. 179–86.

merges again with the wider solar system. Thus, there are subsystems which branch off from the wider solar or galactic system, remain quasi-closed for a limited period of time, and then merge again with the wider system from which they had been separated. Following Reichenbach,[2] we shall use the term "branch system" to designate this kind of subsystem.

Branch systems are formed not only in the natural course of things, but also through human intervention: when an ice cube is placed in a glass of warm gingerale by a waiter and then covered for hygienic purposes, a subsystem has been formed. The prior freezing of the ice cube had involved an entropy increase through the dissipation of electrical energy in some larger quasi-closed system of which the electrically run refrigerator is a part. While the ice cube melts in the covered glass sub-system, that quasi-closed system increases its entropy. But it merges again with another system when the then chilled gingerale is consumed by a person. Similarly for a cold room that is closed off and then heated by burning logs.

Thus our environment abounds in branch systems whose initial rela-tively low entropies are the products of their earlier coupling or inter-action with outside agencies of one kind or another. This rather constant and ubiquitous formation of a branch system in a relatively low entropy state resulting from interaction often proceeds at the expense of an entropy increase in some wider quasi-closed system from which it originated. And the *de facto*, nomologically contingent occurrence of these branch systems has the following *fundamental consequence*, at least for our region of the universe and during the current epoch: among the quasi-closed systems whose entropy is relatively low and which behave as if they might remain isolated, the vast majority have not been and will not remain permanently closed systems, being branch systems instead.

Hence, upon encountering a quasi-closed system in a state of fairly *low* entropy, we know the following to be overwhelmingly probable: the system has *not* been isolated for millions and millions of years and does *not* just *happen* to be in one of the infrequent but ever-recurring low-entropy states exhibited by a permanently isolated system. Instead, our system was formed not too long ago by branching off after an inter-action with an outside agency. For example, suppose that an American geologist is wandering in an isolated portion of the Sahara desert in

[2] Cf. H. Reichenbach, *The Direction of Time*, Berkeley, University of California Press, 1956, p. 118.

search of an oasis and encounters a portion of the sand in the shape of the words "Coca-Cola." He would then infer that, with overwhelming probability, a kindred person had interacted with the sand in the recent past by tracing "Coca-Cola" in it. The geologist would not suppose that he was in the presence of one of those relatively low-entropy configurations which are assumed by the sand particles spontaneously but very rarely, if beaten about by winds for millions upon millions of years in a state of effective isolation from the remainder of the world.

There is a further *de facto* property of branch systems that concerns us. For it will turn out to enter into the temporally asymmetrical statistical regularities which we shall find to be exhibited in the entropic behavior of these systems. This property consists in the following *randomness* obtaining *as a matter of nomologically-contingent fact* in the distribution of the W_1 micro-states belonging to the initial macro-states of a *space* ensemble of branch systems each of which has the same initial entropy $S_1 = k \log W_1$. For each class of *like* branch-systems having the *same* initial entropy value S_1, the micro-states constituting the identical initial macro-states of entropy S_1 are *random samples* of the set of all W_1 micro-states yielding a macro-state of entropy S_1.[3] This attribute of randomness of micro-states on the part of the initial states of the members of the *space* ensemble will be recognized as the counterpart of the following attribute of the micro-states of one single, permanently closed system: there is equiprobability of occurrence among the W_1 micro-states belonging to the *time* ensemble of states of equal entropy $S_1 = k \log W_1$ exhibited by one single, permanently closed system.

We can now state the statistical regularities which obtain as a consequence of the *de facto* properties of branch systems just set forth, when coupled with the principles of statistical mechanics. These regularities, which will be seen to yield a temporally asymmetric behavior of the entropy of *branch* systems, fall into two main groups as follows.

GROUP 1: In most space ensembles of quasi-closed branch systems, each of which is initially in a state of non-equilibrium or relatively *low* entropy, the majority of branch systems in the ensemble will have *higher* entropies *after* a given time t.[4] But these branch systems simply did not exist as quasi-closed, distinct systems at a time t *prior to* the occurrence

---

[3] Cf. R. C. Tolman, *The Principles of Statistical Mechanics*, Oxford, 1938, p. 149.
[4] Cf. R. Fürth, "Prinzipien der Statistik," *Handbuch der Physik*, vol. 4, 1929, pp. 270 and 192–93.

of their initial, branching-off states. Hence, not existing then as such, the branch systems did in fact *not* also exhibit the same higher entropy states at the *earlier* times t, which they would indeed have done then had they existed as closed systems all along.

The increase after a time t in the entropy of the overwhelming majority of branch systems of initially low entropy—as confirmed abundantly by observation—can be made fully intelligible. To do so, we note the following property of the *time* ensemble of entropy values belonging to a single, permanently closed system and then affirm that property of the space ensembles of branch systems: since *large* entropic downgrades or decreases are *far less* probable (frequent) than moderate ones, the *vast majority* of *non*-equilibrium entropy states of a permanently closed system are located either at or in the immediate temporal vicinity of the *bottom* of a *dip* of the one-system entropy curve. In short, the vast majority of the *sub*-maximum entropy states are on or temporally very near the *upgrades* of the one-system curve. The application of this result to the space ensemble of branch systems whose initial states exhibit the aforementioned *de facto* property of randomness then yields the following: among the initial low entropy states of these systems, the vast majority lie at or in the immediate temporal vicinity of the bottoms of the one-system entropy curve at which an upgrade begins.

GROUP 2: A decisive *temporal asymmetry* in the statistics of the temporal evolution of branch systems arises from the further result that in most space ensembles of branch systems, each of whose members is initially in a state of *equilibrium* or very *high* entropy, the vast majority of these systems in the ensemble will *not* have *lower* entropies *after* a finite time t, but will still be in equilibrium.[5] For the aforementioned randomness property assures that the vast majority of those branch systems whose initial states are equilibrium states have maximum entropy values lying somewhere *well within* the plateau of the one-system entropy curve, rather than at the extremity of the plateau at which an entropy *decrease* is initiated.[6]

[5] *Ibid.*, p. 270.

[6] Although the decisive asymmetry just noted was admitted by H. Mehlberg ("Physical Laws and Time's Arrow," in Herbert Feigl and Grover Maxwell, editors, *Current Issues in the Philosophy of Science*, New York, Holt, Rinehart & Winston, 1961, p. 129), he dismisses it as expressing "merely the factual difference between the two relevant values of probability." But an asymmetry is no less an asymmetry for depending on *de facto*, nomologically contingent boundary conditions rather than

We see therefore that in the vast majority of branch systems, either one end of their finite entropy curves is a point of low entropy and the other a point of high entropy, or they are in equilibrium states at both ends as well as during the intervening interval. And it is likewise apparent that the statistical distribution of these entropy values on the time axis is such that the vast majority of branch systems have the *same direction of entropy increase* and hence also the same opposite direction of entropy decrease. Thus, the statistics of entropy increase among branch systems assure that in most space ensembles the vast majority of branch systems will increase their entropy in *one* of the two opposite time directions and decrease it in the other. In this way the entropic behavior of branch systems confers the same statistical anisotropy on the vast majority of all those epochs of time during which the universe exhibits the requisite disequilibrium and contains branch systems satisfying initial conditions of "randomness".[7]

Let us now call the direction of entropy increase of a *typical representative* of these epochs the direction of "later," as indeed we have done from the outset by the mere assignment of higher time numbers in that direction but *without* prejudice to our findings concerning the issue of the anisotropy of time. Then our results pertaining to the entropic behavior of branch systems show that the directions of "earlier than" and

---

being assured by a *law* alone. Since our verification of laws generally has the same partial and indirect character as that of our confirmation of the existence of certain complicated *de facto* boundary conditions, the assertion of an asymmetry depending on *de facto* conditions is generally no less reliable than one wholly grounded on a law. Hence when Mehlberg [*op. cit.*, p. 117, n. 30] urges against Schrödinger's claim of asymmetry that for every pair of branch systems which change their entropy in one direction, "there is nothing to prevent" another pair of closed subsystems from changing their entropy in the opposite direction, the reply is: Mehlberg's criticism can be upheld only by gratuitously neglecting the statistical asymmetry admitted but then dismissed by him as "merely" factual. For a more detailed criticism of Mehlberg's denial of temporal anisotropy, see A. Grünbaum, *Philosophical Problems of Space and Time*, New York, Alfred A. Knopf (in press), Chapter 8.

[7] Readers familiar with Reichenbach's "hypothesis of the branch structure" as set forth in his *The Direction of Time* (p. 136) will note that, though heavily indebted to Reichenbach, my treatment of the assumptions regarding branch systems departs from Reichenbach's in several *essential* respects. A statement and justification of these departures is given in A. Grünbaum, "Carnap's Views on the Foundations of Geometry," n. 97, in P. A. Schilpp, editor, *The Philosophy of Rudolf Carnap*, La Salle, Illinois, Open Court Publishing Co., 1963.

"later than" are not merely opposite directions bearing decreasing and increasing time co-ordinates respectively but are statistically *anisotropic* in an objective physical sense.[8]

We are now prepared to elucidate the bearing of this conclusion on the conditions under which there is asymmetry between retrodiction and prediction.

Suppose we encounter a beach whose sand forms a smooth surface except for one place where it is in the shape of a human footprint. We know from our previous considerations with high probability that instead of having evolved *isolatedly* from a prior state of uniform smoothness into its present uneven configuration according to the statistical entropy principle for a permanently closed system, the beach was an *open* system in *interaction* with a stroller. And we are aware furthermore that if there is some quasi-closed wider system containing the beach and the stroller, as there often is, the beach achieved its ordered low-entropy state of bearing the imprint or interaction-indicator at the expense of an at least compensatory entropy increase in that wider system comprising the stroller: the stroller increased the entropy of the wider system by scattering his energy reserves in making the footprint.

We see that the sandy footprint shape is a genuine indicator and not a randomly achieved form resulting from the unperturbed chance concatenations of the grains of sand. The imprint thus contains information in the sense of being a veridical indicator of an interaction. Now, in all probability the entropy of the imprint-bearing beach system increases after the interaction with the stroller through the smoothing action of the wind. And this entropy increase is parallel, in all probability, to the direction of entropy increase of the majority of branch systems. Moreover, we saw that the production of the indicator by the interaction is likely to have involved an entropy increase in some wider system of which the indicator is a part. Hence, *in all probability the states of the interacting systems which do contain the indicators of the interaction are the relatively*

---

[8] This is *not* to say that entropic changes are the *sole* source of the anisotropy of time. But processes which are *de facto* irreversible though *not* involving any entropy increase [Cf. K. R. Popper, "The Arrow of Time," *Nature*, vol. 177, p. 538, and vol. 178, p. 382, 1956; E. L. Hill and A. Grünbaum, "Irreversible Processes in Physical Theory," *Nature*, vol. 179, p. 1296, 1957; and A. Grünbaum, "Popper on Irreversibility," in M. Bunge, editor, *The Critical Approach: Essays in Honor of Karl Popper*, New York, The Free Press of Glencoe (in press)] are *not* of importance for the asymmetry between retrodiction and prediction, which is our guiding concern in this section.

higher entropy states of the majority of branch systems, as compared to the interaction state. Hence the indicator states are the relatively later states as compared to the states of interaction which they attest. And by being both *later* and indicators, these states have *retrodictive* significance, thereby being traces, records, or memories. And due to the high degree of retrodictive univocity of the low-entropy states constituting the indicators, the latter are veridical to a high degree of *specificity*.

Confining our attention for the present to indicators whose *production* requires only the occurrence of the interaction which they attest, we therefore obtain the following conclusion. Apart from two classes of *advance* indicators requiring very special conditions for their production and constituting *exceptions*, it is the case that *with overwhelming probability, low entropy indicator states can exist in systems whose interactions they attest only after and not before these interactions.*[9] If this conclusion is true (assuming that there are either no cases or not enough cases of *bona fide* precognition to disconfirm it), then, of course, it is not an a priori truth. And it would be very shallow indeed to seek to construe it as a trivial a priori truth in the following way: calling the indicator states "traces," "records," or "memories" and noting that it then becomes tautological to assert that traces and the like have only retrodictive and no predictive significance. But this transparent verbal gambit cannot make it true a priori that— apart from the exceptions to be dealt with below—interacting systems bear indicators attesting veridically only their *earlier* and *not* their later interactions with outside agencies.

Hence, the two exceptions apart, we arrive at the fundamental asymmetry of recordability: *reliable indicators in interacting systems permit only retrodictive inferences concerning the interactions for which they vouch but no predictive inferences pertaining to corresponding later interactions.*

The logical schema of these inductive inferences is roughly as follows: The premises assert (1) the presence of a certain relatively low entropy state in the system, and (2) a quasi-universal statistical law stating that most low-entropy states are interaction indicators *and* were *preceded* by the

---

[9] The two exceptions, which we shall discuss in some detail below, are constituted by the following two classes of advance indicators: (1) veridical predictions made and stored (recorded) by human (or other sentient, theory-using) beings, and physically registered, *bona fide* advance indicators produced by computers; and (2) advance indicators (e.g., sudden barometric drops) which are produced by the very cause (pressure change) that also produces the future interaction (storm) indicated by them.

interactions for which they vouch. The conclusion from these premises is then the inductive retrodictive one that there was an earlier interaction of a certain kind.

As already mentioned, our affirmation of the temporal asymmetry of recordability of interactions must be qualified by dealing with two exceptional cases, the first of which is the pre-recordability of those inter-actions which are veridically predicted by human beings (or computers), For any event which could be predicted by a scientist could also be "pre-recorded" by that scientist in various forms such as a written entry on paper asserting its occurrence at a certain later time, an advance drawing, or even an advance photograph based on the pre-drawing. By the same token, artifacts like computers can pre-record events which they can predict. A comparison between the written, drawn, or photographic pre-record (i.e., recorded prediction) of, say, the crash of a plane into a house and its post-record in the form of a caved-in house, and a like comparison of the corresponding pre- and post-records of the interaction of a foot with a beach will now enable us to formulate the essential differences in the conditions requisite to the respective production of pre-records and post-records as well as the usual differences in make-up between them.

The production of at least one retrodictive indicator or post-record of an interaction such as the plane's crash into the house requires only the occurrence of that interaction (as well as a moderate degree of durability of the record). The retrodictive indicator states in the system which inter-acted with an outside agency must, of course, be distinguished from the *epistemic use* which human beings may make of these physical indicator states. And our assertion of the sufficiency of the interaction for the pro-duction of a post-record allows, of course, that the *interpretation* of actual post-records by humans as *bona fide* documents of the past requires their use of theory and not just the occurrence of the interaction. In contrast to the sufficiency of an interaction itself for its (at least short-lived) post-recordability, no such sufficiency obtains in the case of the pre-record-ability of an interaction: save for an overwhelmingly improbable freak occurrence, the production of even a single pre-record of the coupling of a system with an agency external to it requires, as a necessary condition, *either* (a) the use of an appropriate theory by symbol-using entities (humans, computers) having suitable information; *or* (b) the pre-record's being a partial effect of a cause that also produces the pre-recorded interaction, as in the barometric case to be dealt with below. And in contexts in which (a) is a necessary condition, we find the following: Since pre-records are, by definition, veridical, this necessary condition cannot *generally* also be sufficient, unless the predictive theory employed is deterministic *and* the information available to the theory-using organism pertains to a closed system.

In addition to differing in regard to the conditions of their production, pre-records generally differ from post-records in the following further respect: unless the pre-record prepared by a human being (or computer) *happens* to be part of the interacting system to which it pertains, the pre-record will not be contained in states of the interacting system which it concerns but will be in some other system. Thus, a pre-record of the crash of a plane into a house in a heavy fog would generally *not* be a part of either the house or the plane, although it can happen to be. But in the case of *post*-recording, there will always be at least one post-record however short-lived, in the interacting system itself to which that post-record pertains.

Our earlier example of the footprint on the beach will serve to illustrate more fully the asymmetry between the requirements for the production of a pre-record and of a post-record. The pre-recording of a *later* incursion of the beach by a stroller would require extensive information about the motivations and habits of people not now at the beach and also knowledge of the accessibility of the beach to prospective strollers. This is tantamount to knowledge of a large system which is *closed*, so that all relevant agencies can safely be presumed to have been included in it. For otherwise, we would be unable to guarantee, for example, that the *future* stroller will *not* be stopped enroute to the beach by some agency not included in the system, an eventuality whose occurrence would deprive our pre-record of its referent, thereby destroying its status as a veridical indicator. In short, in the case of the footprint, which is a post-record and *not* a pre-record of the interaction of a human foot with the beach, the interaction itself is *sufficient* for its post-recording (though not for the extended *durability* of the record once it exists) but *not* for its pre-recording and prediction. Since a future interaction of a potentially open system like the beach is *not* itself sufficient for its pre-recordability, open systems like beaches therefore do not themselves exhibit pre-records of their own future interactions. Instead—apart from the second species of pre-recordability to be considered presently—pre-recordability of interactions of potentially open systems requires the mediation of symbol-

and theory-using organisms or the operation of appropriate artifacts like computers. And such pre-recordability can obtain successfully only if the theory available to the pre-recording organism is deterministic and sufficiently comprehensive to include all the relevant laws and boundary conditions governing the pertinent closed systems.

The second species of exceptions to the asymmetry of recordability is exemplified by the fact that a sudden drop in the pressure reading of a barometer can be an advance indicator or "pre-record" of a subsequent storm. To be sure, it is the immediately *prior* pressure change in the spatial vicinity of the barometer and only that particular prior change (i.e., the *past* interaction through pressure) which is recorded numerically by a given drop in the barometric reading, and *not* the pressure change that *will* exist at the same place at a *later* time. To make the predictions required for a *pre*-recording of the pressure changes which will exist at a given space point at later times (i.e., of the corresponding future inter-actions), comprehensive meteorological data pertaining to a large region would be essential. *But* it *is* possible in this case to base a rather reliable prediction of a future storm on the present sudden barometric drop. The latter drop, however, is, in fact, a *bona fide* advance indicator *only because* it is a partial effect of the very comprehensive cause which also produces (assures) the storm. Thus, it is the fulfillment of the *necessary condition* of having a causal ancestry that overlaps with that of the storm which is needed to confer the status of an advance indicator on the barometric drop. In contrast to the situation prevailing in the case of *post*-recordability, the exis-tence of this necessary condition makes for the fact that the future occurrence of a storm is *not sufficient* for the existence of an advance indicator of that storm in the form of a sudden barometric drop at an earlier time.

An analogous account can be given of the following cases, which Mr. F. Brian Skyrms has suggested to me for consideration: situations in which *human intentions* are highly reliable advance indicators of the events en-visaged by these intentions. Thus, the desire for a glass of beer, coupled with the supposed presence of the conditions under which beer and a glass are obtainable, produces as a partial effect the intent to get it. And, *if* external conditions permit (the beer is available and accessible), and, furthermore, if the required internal conditions materialize (the person desiring the beer remains able to go and get it), then the intent will issue in the obtaining and drinking of the beer. But in contrast to the situation prevailing in the case of retrodictive indicators (post-records), the future consumption of the beer is *not* a *sufficient condition* for the existence of its probabilistic advance indicator in the form of an intention.

The consideration of some alleged counter-examples will serve to complete our statement of the temporal asymmetry of the recordability of interactions. These purported counter-examples are to the effect that there are pre-records *not* depending for their production on the use of predictive theory by symbol-using organisms, or on the pre-record's being a partial effect of a cause that also produces the pre-recorded interaction.

In the first place, it might be argued that there are spontaneous pre-records as exemplified in the following two kinds of scientific contexts: (1) in any essentially closed dynamical system such as the solar system, a dynamical state later than one occurring at a time t_0 is a *sufficient condition* for the occurrence of the state at time t_0, no less than is a state prior to t_0; hence the state at time t_0 can be regarded as a *pre*-record of the later state no less than it can be deemed a post-record of the earlier one; and (2) a certain kind of death—say, the kind of death ensuing from leukemia—may be a sufficient condition for the existence of a pre-record of it in the form of the onset of active leukemia. But these examples violate the conditions on which our denial of spontaneous pre-recordability is predicated in the following essential respect: they involve later states which are *not* states of *interaction* with outside agencies entered into by an otherwise closed system, in the manner of our example of the beach.

In the second place, since the thesis of the temporal asymmetry of spontaneous recordability makes cases of *bona fide* precognition overwhelmingly improbable, it might be said that this thesis and the entropic considerations undergirding it are vulnerable to the discovery of a reasonable number of cases of genuine precognition, a discovery which is claimed by some to have already been made. To this I retort that if the purported occurrence of precognition turns out to become well authenticated, then I am, of course, prepared to envision such alterations in the body of current orthodox scientific theory as may be required.

III

THE BEARING OF THE RETRODICTION-PREDICTION ASYMMETRY ON THE ISSUE
OF SYMMETRY BETWEEN EXPLANATION AND PREDICTION

In section I, we gave a preliminary demarcation of the retrodiction-prediction antithesis from the explanation-prediction distinction as understood by writers such as Hempel.[10] We shall now complete that demarcation and will then represent the results on a diagram.

For Hempel, the particular conditions C_i ($i = 1, 2, \ldots n$) which, in conjunction with the relevant laws, account for the *explanandum*-event E may be *earlier* than E in *both* explanation *and* prediction, or the C_i may be *later* than E in *both* explanation and prediction. Thus, a case of *prediction* in which the C_i would be *later* than E would be one in astronomy, for example, in which a future E is accounted for by reference to C_i which are still further in the future than E. These assertions hold, since Hempel's criterion for an explanation as opposed to a prediction is that E belong to the scientist's *past* when he offers his account of it, and his criterion for a corresponding prediction is that E belong to the scientist's *future* when it is made.

On the other hand, in the retrodiction-prediction antithesis, a *retrodiction* is characterized by the fact that the C_i are *later* than E, while the C_i are *earlier* than E in the kind of *prediction* which is antithetical to retrodiction but *not* identical with Hempelian prediction.

In the accompanying diagram, the i, k, l, m may each range over the values 1, 2, ... n.

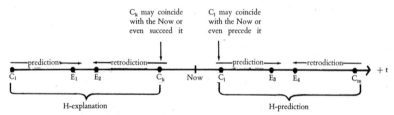

If we use the pre-fix "H" as an abbreviation for "Hempelian," then two consequences are apparent. First, a retrodiction as well as a prediction can be an H-prediction, and a prediction as well as a retrodiction can be an H-explanation. Secondly, being an H-prediction rather than an H-explanation or conversely depends on the transient homocentric "now," but there is no such "now"-dependence in the case of being a retrodiction instead of a prediction, or conversely.

---

[10] I refer here to the original paper of C. G. Hempel and P. Oppenheim: "Studies in the Logic of Explanation," *Philosophy of Science*, vol. 15, 135 (1948). For Hempel's most recent statement of his account of scientific explanation, see his "Deductive Nomological vs. Statistical Explanation," in H. Feigl and G. Maxwell, editors, *Minnesota Studies in the Philosophy of Science*, vol. 3, Minneapolis, University of Minnesota Press, 1962.

The passage in the Hempel–Oppenheim essay setting forth the symmetry thesis espoused by K. R. Popper and these authors reads as follows:

> ... the same formal analysis, including the four necessary conditions, applies to scientific prediction as well as to explanation. The difference between the two is of a pragmatic character. If E is given, i.e., if we know that the phenomenon described by E has occurred, and a suitable set of statements $C_1, C_2, ... , C_k, L_1, L_2, ... , L_r$ is provided afterwards, we speak of an explanation of the phenomenon in question. If the latter statements are given and E is derived prior to the occurrence of the phenomenon it describes, we speak of a prediction. It may be said, therefore, that an explanation is not fully adequate unless its explanans, if taken account of in time, could have served as a basis for predicting the phenomenon under consideration.[11]—Consequently, whatever will be said in this article concerning the logical characteristics of explanation or prediction will be applicable to either, even if only one of them should be mentioned.[12]

Hempel's thesis of symmetry or structural equality between H-explanation and H-prediction can therefore now be formulated in the following way: Any *prediction* which qualifies logically *and* methodologically as an H-explanation also qualifies as an H-prediction, provided that the scientist is in possession of the information concerning the C_i prior to the occurrence of E, and conversely. And any *retrodiction* which qualifies logically *and* methodologically as an H-explanation also qualifies as an H-prediction, provided that the information concerning the relevant C_i is available at an appropriate time, and conversely.

Before examining critically the diverse objections which have been leveled against Hempel's thesis of symmetry in the recent literature by N. Rescher,[13] S. F. Barker,[14] N. R. Hanson,[15] and M. Scriven,[16] I wish

---

[11] "The logical similarity of explanation and prediction, and the fact that one is directed towards past occurrences, the other towards future ones, is well expressed in the terms 'postdictability' and 'predictability' used by Reichenbach in [*Quantum Mechanics*], p. 13."

[12] C. G. Hempel and P. Oppenheim, *op. cit.*, sec. 3.

[13] N. Rescher, "On Prediction and Explanation," *British Journal for the Philosophy of Science*, vol. 8, 281 (1958).

[14] S. F. Barker, "The Role of Simplicity in Explanation," in: *Current Issues in the Philosophy of Science* (editors, Feigl and Maxwell), New York, 1961, pp. 265–86, and the Comments on this paper by Salmon, Feyerabend and Rudner with Barker's Rejoinders.

to make a few remarks concerning my construal both of that thesis and of the philosophical task to whose fulfillment it pertains.

I take Hempel's affirmation of symmetry to pertain *not* to the *assertibility per se* of the *explanandum* but to the either deductive or inductive *inferability* of the *explanandum* from the *explanans*. Popper and Hempel say: To the extent that there is ever explanatory *inferability*, there is also predictive inferability and conversely. They do *not* claim that every time you are entitled to *assert, on some grounds or other,* that a certain kind of event *did* occur in the past, you are *also* entitled to say that the same kind of event *will* occur in the future. Being concerned with scientific understanding, Popper and Hempel say that there is temporal symmetry *not* of assertibility *per se* but of assertibility on the strength of the *explanans*. The *scientific* relevance of dealing with predictive *arguments* rather than mere predictive assertions can hardly be contested by claiming with Scriven that in this context "the crucial point is that, however achieved, a prediction is what it is simply because it is produced in advance of the event it predicts; it is *intrinsically* nothing but a bare description of that event."[17] For surely a soothsayer's unsupported prophecy that there will not be a third world war is not of scientific significance and ought not to command any scientific interest precisely because of the unreasoned manner of its achievement. Hence a scientifically warranted prediction of an event must be more than a mere pre-assertion of the event. And in any context which is to be scientifically relevant, the following two components can be distinguished in the meaning of the term "H-predict" no less than in the meaning of "H-explain ' (or "post-explain"), and similarly for the corresponding nouns:

1. The mere *assertion* of the *explanandum*, which *may* be based on grounds other than its scientific *explanans*.

2. The logical *derivation* (deductive or inductive) of the *explanandum* from an *explanans*, the character of the content of the *explanans* remaining unspecified until later on in this essay.

My attachment of the prefix "H" to the word "explain" (and to

[15] N. R. Hanson, "On the Symmetry Between Explanation and Prediction," *The Philosophical Review*, vol. 68, 349 (1959).

[16] M. Scriven, "Explanation and Prediction in Evolutionary Theory," *Science*, vol. 130, 477 (1959), and "Explanations, Predictions and Laws," in H. Feigl and G. Maxwell, editors, *Minnesota Studies in the Philosophy of Science*, vol. 3, 1962.

[17] M. Scriven, "Explanations, Predictions and Laws," *op. cit.*, sec. 3.4.

"explanation") and my use of "post-explain" as a synonym of "H-explain" will serve to remind us for the sake of clarity that this usage of "explain" results from a restriction to the past of *one* well-established usage which is *temporally-neutral*, viz., "explain" in the sense of providing scientific understanding (or a scientific accounting) of why something did *or* will occur. But, to my mind, the philosophical task before us is *not* the ascertainment of how the *words* "explain" and "predict" are used, even assuming that there is enough consistency and precision in their usage to make this lexicographic task feasible. And hence the verdict on the correctness of Hempel's symmetry thesis cannot be made to depend on whether it holds for what is taken to be the actual or ordinary usage of these terms. Instead, in this context I conceive the philosophical task to be both the elucidation and examination of the provision of scientific understanding of an *explanandum* by an *explanans* as encountered in actual scientific theory. Accordingly, Hempel's symmetry thesis, which concerns the inferability of the *explananda* from a given kind of *explanans* and *not* their assertibility, must be assessed on the basis of a comparison of H-predictive with H-explanatory *arguments* with respect to the measure of scientific understanding afforded by them. Thus, the issue of the adequacy of the symmetry thesis will revolve around whether there is temporal symmetry in regard to the degree of entailment, as it were, characterizing the logical link between the *explanans* and the *explanandum*. Specifically, we shall need to answer both of the following questions: (1) Would the type of *argument* which yields a prediction of a future *explanandum*-event not furnish precisely the same amount of scientific understanding of a corresponding past event? (2) Does an *explanans* explain an *explanandum* referring to a past event any more conclusively than this same kind of *explanans* predictively implies the *explanandum* pertaining to the corresponding future event?

We are now ready to turn to the appraisal of the criticisms of Hempel's symmetry thesis offered by Rescher, Barker, Hanson, and Scriven. In the light of my formulation of Hempel's thesis, it becomes clear that it does *not* assert, as Rescher supposes, that any set of C_i which permit a *predictive* inference also qualify for a corresponding *retrodictive* one, or that the converse is true. As Rescher notes correctly but irrelevantly, whether or not symmetry obtains between prediction and retrodiction in any given domain of empirical science is indeed *not* a purely logical question but depends on the content of the laws pertaining to the domain in question.

We see therefore that Hempel was justified in claiming[18] that Rescher has confused H-explanation with retrodiction. And this confusion is also facilitated by one of Scriven's statements of the symmetry thesis, which reads[19]: "to predict, we need a correlation between present events and future ones—to explain, between present ones and past ones."

In agreement with Scheffler,[20] Rescher offers a further criticism of the Hempelian assertion of symmetry: "it is inconsistent with scientific custom and usage regarding the concepts of explanation and prediction," for, among other things, "Only true statements are proper objects for explanation, but clearly not so with prediction."[21] And in support of the latter claim of an *"epistemological asymmetry,"* Rescher points to a large number of cases in which we have "virtually certain knowledge of the past on the basis of traces found in the present" but "merely probable knowledge of the future on the basis of knowledge of the present and/or the past."[22]

The question raised by Rescher's further objection is whether this *epistemological* asymmetry can be held to impugn the Hempelian thesis of symmetry. To deal with this question, it is fundamental to distinguish —as Rescher, Barker, Hanson, and Scriven unfortunately *failed* to do, much to the detriment of their theses—between the following two sets of ideas: (1) an asymmetry between H-explanation and H-prediction both in regard to the *grounds* on which we claim to know *that* the *explanandum* is *true* and correlatively in regard to the *degree* of our *confidence* in the supposed truth of the *explanandum*; and (2) an asymmetry, *if any*, between H-explanation and H-prediction with respect to the *logical relation* obtaining between the *explanans* and the *explanandum*. For the sake of brevity, we shall refer to the *first* asymmetry as pertaining to the *"assertibility"* of the *explanandum* while speaking of the second as an asymmetry in the *"inferability"* or *"why"* of the *explanandum*. In the light of this distinction, we shall be able to show that the existence of an epistemological asymmetry in regard to the assertibility of the *explanandum cannot* serve to impugn the Hempelian thesis of symmetry, which pertains to only the *why* of the *explanandum*.

---

[18] Hempel, "Deductive-Nomological vs. Statistical Explanation," *op. cit.*, sec. 6.
[19] Scriven, "Explanation and Prediction in Evolutionary Theory," *op. cit.*, p. 479.
[20] I. Scheffler, "Explanation, Prediction and Abstraction," *British J. Phil. of. Science*, vol. 7, 293 (1957).
[21] Rescher, *op. cit.*, p. 282.   [22] *Ibid.*, p. 284.

If understood as pertaining to the *assertibility* of the *explanandum*, Rescher's contention of the existence of an epistemological asymmetry is indeed correct. For we saw in section II that there are *highly reliable* records of past interactions but no spontaneously produced records of corresponding future interactions. And this fact has the important consequence that while we can certify the *assertibility* or truth of an *explanandum* referring to a *past* interaction on the basis of a record *without* invoking the supposed truth of any (usual) *explanans* thereof, generally no pre-indicator but only the supposed truth of an appropriate *explanans* can be invoked to vouch for the assertibility or truth of the *explanandum* pertaining to a *future* interaction. And since the theory underlying our interpretations of records is confirmed better than are many of the theories used in an *explanans*, there is a very large class of cases in which an epistemological asymmetry does obtain with respect to the assertibility of the *explanandum*. But this asymmetry of assertibility cannot detract from the following symmetry affirmed by Popper and Hempel: you can post-assert an *explanandum on the strength of its explanans* no better than you can pre-assert it.

The entire substance of both Barker's objection to Hempelian symmetry and Hanson's (1959) critique of it is vitiated by the following fact: these authors adduced what they failed to recognize as a temporal asymmetry in the mere assertibility of the *explanandum* to claim against Hempel that there is a temporal asymmetry in the *why*. And they did so by citing cases in which they invoke a spurious contrast between the *non-assertibility* of an *explanandum* referring to the future and the *inductive inferability* of the corresponding *explanandum* pertaining to the past. Thus we find that Barker writes: "it can be correct to speak of explanation in many cases where specific prediction is not possible. Thus, for instance, if the patient shows all the symptoms of pneumonia, sickens and dies, I can then explain his death—I know what killed him—but I could not have definitely predicted in advance that he was going to die; for usually pneumonia fails to be fatal."[23] But all that Barker is entitled to here is the following claim, which is wholly compatible with Hempel's symmetry thesis: in many cases such as the pneumonia one, there obtains post-assertibility of the *explanandum* but no corresponding pre-assertibility because of the asymmetry of spontaneous recordability. But this does *not*, of course, justify the contention that a past death, which did materialize and is reliably known from a record, can be *explained* by reference to

[23] Barker, *op. cit.*, p. 271.

earlier pneumonia any more conclusively than a future death can be *inferred predictively* on the basis of a present state of pneumonia. For the logical link between the *explanans* affirming a *past* state of pneumonia and the *explanandum* stating the recorded (known) death of a pneumonia patient is precisely the *same* inductive one as in the case of the corresponding avowedly probabilistic *predictive* inference (H-prediction) of death on the basis of an *explanans* asserting a patient's *present* affliction with pneumonia.

It would seem that the commission of Barker's error of affirming an asymmetry in the *why* is facilitated by the following question-begging difference between the *explanans* used in his H-explanation of a death from pneumonia and the one used by him in the purportedly corresponding prediction: Barker's H-explanation of the past death employs an *explanans* asserting the onset of pneumonia at a past time as well as the *sickening* at a later past time, but the further condition of sickening is omitted from the antecedents of his corresponding H-prediction. Hence the spurious asymmetry of conclusiveness between the two cases.

It is now apparent that the valid core of Barker's statement is the common-place that in the pneumonia case, as in others, post-assertibility of the *explanandum* does obtain even though pre-assertibility does not. And once it is recognized that the only relevant asymmetry which does obtain in cases of the pneumonia type is one of assertibility, the philosophical challenge of this asymmetry is to specify the complex *reasons* for it, as I have endeavored to do in section II above. But no philosophical challenge is posed for Hempel's symmetry thesis.

An analogous confusion between the assertibility asymmetry and one in the *why* invalidates the paper by Hanson which Barker cites in support of his views. Suppose that a certain kind of past measurement yielded a particular ψ-function which is then used in Schrödinger's equation for the H-explanation of a later past occurrence. And suppose also that the same kind of present measurement again yields the same ψ-function for a like system and that this function is then used for the H-prediction of a correspondingly later future occurrence, which is of the same type as the past occurrence. It is patent that in quantum mechanics the *logical relation* between *explanans* (the function ψ_1 and the associated set s_1 of probability distributions at the time t_1) and *explanandum* (the description of a *particular* micro-event falling within the range of one of the s_1 probability distributions) is no less statistical (inductive) in the case of H-explanation than in the case of H-prediction. And this *symmetry* in the *statistical why* is wholly compatible with the following asymmetry: the reliability of our knowledge *that* a specific kind of micro-event belonging to the range of one of the s₁ probability distributions *has* occurred in the past has no counterpart in our knowledge of the *future* occurrence of such an event, because only the results of *past* measurements (interactions) are available in records. Hence it was wholly amiss for Hanson to have used the latter asymmetry of recordability as a basis for drawing a pseudo-contrast between the quantum mechanical *inferability* of a *past* micro-event—this inferability being logically identical with that of a future one—and the lack of *pre-assertibility* of the future occurrence of the micro-event. Says he: "any single quantum phenomenon P ... can be completely *explained ex post facto*; one can *understand* fully just what kind of event occurred, in terms of the well-established laws of the ... quantum theory. ... But it is, of course, the most fundamental feature of these laws that the *prediction* of such a phenomenon P is, as a matter of theoretical principle, quite impossible."[24] Hanson overlooks that the asymmetry between pre-assertibility and post-assertibility obtaining in quantum mechanics in no way makes for an asymmetry between H-explanation and H-prediction with respect to the relation of the *explanandum* to its quantum mechanical *explanans*. And the statistical character of quantum mechanics enters only in the following sense: when coupled with the recordability asymmetry of classical physics, it makes for a temporal asymmetry in the assertibility of the *explanandum*.

We see that the statistical character of the quantum mechanical account of micro-phenomena is no less compatible with the symmetry between H-explanation and H-prediction than is the *deterministic* character of Newton's mechanics. And this result renders untenable what Hanson regards as the upshot of his 1959 paper on the symmetry issue, viz., "that there is a most intimate connection between Hempel's account of the symmetry between explanation and prediction and the logic of Newton's *Principia*."[25]

It remains to deal in some detail with Scriven's extensive critique of Hempel's thesis. Scriven argues that (1) evolutionary explanations and explanations like that of the past occurrence of paresis due to syphilis fail

[24] Hanson, "On the Symmetry Between Explanation and Prediction," *op. cit.*, pp. 353–54.
[25] *Ibid.*, p. 357.

to meet the symmetry requirement by not allowing corresponding predictions; and (2) predictions based on mere *indicators* (rather than causes) such as the prediction of a storm from a sudden barometric drop are not matched by corresponding explanations, since *indicators* are not explanatory though they may serve to predict or, in other cases, to retrodict. And these indicator-based predictions show that the mere inferability of an *explanandum* does *not* guarantee scientific understanding of it, so that symmetry of inferability does not assure symmetry of scientific understanding between explanation and prediction.

I shall now examine several of the paradigm cases adduced by Scriven in support of these contentions.

I. EVOLUTIONARY THEORY

He cites evolutionary theory with the aim of showing that "Satisfactory explanation of the past is possible even when prediction of the future is impossible."[26]

Evolutionary theory does indeed afford valid examples of the epistemological asymmetry of assertibility. And this for the following two reasons growing out of our section II: (1) the ubiquitous role of interactions in evolution brings the recordability asymmetry into play. And that asymmetry enters not only into the assertibility of the *explanandum*. For in cases of an H-prediction based on an *explanans* containing an *antecedent* referring to a *future* interaction, there is also an asymmetry of assertibility between H-prediction and H-explanation in regard to the *explanans*; and (2) the existence of biological properties which are *emergent* in the sense that, even if all the laws were strictly *deterministic*, the occurrence of these properties could *not* have been *predicted* on the basis of any and all laws which could possibly have been discovered by humans in advance of the first known occurrence of the respective properties in question. Thus, evolutionary theory makes us familiar with past biological changes which were induced by prior *past* interactions, the latter being post-assertible on the basis of present records. And these past interactions can serve to explain the evolutionary changes in question. But the logical relation between *explanans* and *explanandum* furnishing this explanation is

---

[26] M. Scriven, "Explanation and Prediction in Evolutionary Theory," *op. cit.*, p. 477.

completely *time-symmetric*. Hence this situation makes for asymmetry only in the following innocuous sense: since corresponding future interactions cannot be rationally pre-asserted—there being no advance records of them—there is no corresponding pre-assertibility of those future evolutionary changes that will be affected by future interactions.

In an endeavor to establish the existence of an asymmetry damaging to Hempel's thesis on the basis of the account of a case of non-survival given in evolutionary theory, Scriven writes:

> ... there are ... good grounds [of inherent unpredictability] for saying that even in principle explanation and prediction do *not* have the same form. Finally, it is not in general possible to list all the exceptions to a claim about, for example, the fatal effects of a lava flow, so we have to leave it in probability form; this has the result of eliminating the very degree of certainty from the prediction that the explanation has, when we find the fossils in the lava.[27]

But all that the lava case entitles Scriven to conclude is that the merely *probabilistic* connection between the occurrence of a lava flow and the extinction of certain organisms has the result of depriving pre-*assertibility* of the very degree of certainty possessed by post-assertions here. Scriven is not at all justified in supposing that *predictive inferability* in this case lacks even an iota of the certainty that can be ascribed to the corresponding post-explanatory inferability. For wherein does the greater degree of certainty of the post-explanation reside? I answer: only in the assertibility of the *explanandum*, *not* in the character of the logical relation between the *explanans* (the lava flow) and the *explanandum* (fatalities on the part of certain organisms). What then must be the verdict on Scriven's contention of an asymmetry in the *certainty* of prediction and post-explanation in this context? We see now that this contention is vitiated by a confusion between the following two radically *distinct* kinds of asymmetry: (1) a difference in the degree of certainty (categoricity) of our knowledge of the truth of the *explanandum* and of the claim of environmental unfitness made by the *explanans*, and (2) a difference in the "degree of entailment," as it were, linking the *explanandum* to the *explanans*.

Very similar difficulties beset Scriven's analysis of a case of biological survival which is accounted for on the basis of environmental fitness. He says:

[27] *Ibid.*, p. 480.

It is fairly obvious that no characteristics can be identified as contributing to "fitness" in all environments. ... We cannot predict which
organisms will survive except in so far as we can predict the environmental changes. But we are very poorly equipped to do this with much
precision.[28] ... However, these difficulties of prediction do not mean
that the idea of fitness as a factor in survival loses all of its *explanatory*
power. ... Animals which happen to be able to swim are better fitted
for surviving a sudden and unprecedented inundation of their arid
habitat, and in some such cases it is just this factor which explains their
survival. Naturally we could have said in advance that *if* a flood
occurred, they would be likely to survive; let us call this a hypothetical
probability prediction. But hypothetical predictions do not have any
value for actual predictions except in so far as the conditions mentioned
in the hypothesis are predictable ... : hence there will be cases where
we can *explain why* certain animals and plants survived even when we
could not have *predicted that* they would.[29]

There would, of course, be complete agreement with Scriven, if he
had been content to point out in this context, as he does, that there are
cases in which we can *"explain why"* but not *"predict that."* But he com-
bines this correct formulation with the incorrect supposition that cases of
post-explaining survival on the basis of fitness constitute grounds for an
indictment of Hempel's thesis of symmetry. Let me therefore state the
points of agreement and disagreement in regard to this case as follows. Once
we recognize the ubiquitous role of *interactions* we can formulate the valid
upshot of Scriven's observations by saying: insofar as future fitness and
survival depend on future interactions which cannot be predicted from
given information, whereas past fitness and survival depended on past
interactions which *can* be retrodicted from that same information, there
is an epistemological asymmetry between H-explanation and H-prediction

---

[28] The environmental changes which Scriven goes on to cite are all of the nature
of *interactions* of a potentially open system. And it is this common property of theirs
which makes for their role in precluding the predictability of survival.

[29] *Ibid.*, p. 478. In a recent paper "Cause and Effect in Biology" [*Science*, vol. 134
(1961), p. 1504], the zoologist E. Mayr overlooks the fallacy of Scriven's statement
which we are about to point out and credits Scriven with having "emphasized quite
correctly that one of the most important contributions to philosophy made by the
evolutionary theory is that it has demonstrated the independence of explanation from
prediction." And Mayr rests this conclusion among other things on the contention
that "the theory of natural selection can describe and explain phenomena with con-
siderable precision, but it cannot make reliable predictions."

in regard to the following: the assertibility both of the antecedent fitness affirmed in the *explanans* and of the *explanandum* claiming survival.

This having been granted as both true and illuminating, we must go on to say at once that the following considerations—which Scriven can grant only on pain of inconsistency with his account of asymmetry in the lava case—are no less true: the scientific inferability from a cause and hence our understanding of the *why* of survival furnished by an *explanans* which *does* contain the antecedent condition that the given animals are able to swim during a sudden, unprecedented inundation of their arid habitat is *not* one iota more probabilistic (i.e., less conclusive) in the case of a *future* inundation and survival than in the case of a *past* one. For if the logical nerve of intelligibility linking the *explanans* (fitness under specified kinds of inundational conditions) with the *explanandum* (survival) is only probabilistic in the *future* case, how could it possibly be any less probabilistic in the past case? It is evident that post-explanatory inductive inferability is entirely on a par here with predictive inferability from fitness as a cause. Why then does Scriven feel entitled to speak of "probability prediction" of *future* survival *without also* speaking of "probability explanation" of past survival? It would seem that his reason is none other than the pseudo-contrast between the *lack* of pre-assertibility of the *explanandum* (which is conveyed by the term "probability" in "probability prediction") and the obtaining of post-explanatory inductive inferability of the *explanandum*. And this pseudo-contrast derives its plausibility from the tacit appeal to the *bona fide* asymmetry between the pre-assertibility and post-assertibility of the *explanandum*, an asymmetry which cannot score against Hempel's thesis.

2. THE PARESIS CASE

In a further endeavor to justify his repudiation of Hempel's thesis, Scriven says:

> ... we can explain but not predict whenever we have a proposition of the form "The only cause of X is A" (I)—for example, "The only cause of paresis is syphilis." Notice that this is perfectly compatible with the statement that A is often not followed by X—in fact, very few syphilitics develop paresis (II). Hence, when A is observed, we can predict that X is *more* likely to occur than without A, but still extremely unlikely. So, we must, on the evidence, still predict that it will *not*

occur. But if it does, we can appeal to (I) to provide and guarantee our explanation. ... Hence an event which cannot be predicted from a certain set of well-confirmed propositions can, if it occurs, be explained by appeal to them.[30]

In short, Scriven's argument is that although a past case of paresis can be explained by noting that syphilis was its cause, one cannot predict the future occurrence of paresis from syphilis as the cause. And he adds to this the following oral comment:

> Suppose for the moment we include the justification of an explanation or a prediction in the explanation or prediction, as Hempel does. From a general law and antecedent conditions we are then entitled to deduce that a certain event will occur in the future. This is the deduction of a prediction. From one of the propositions of the form the only possible cause of y is x and a statement that y has occurred we are able to deduce, not only that x must have occurred, but also the proposition the cause of y in this instance was x. I take this to be a perfectly sound example of deducing and explanation. Notice however, that what we have deduced is not at all a description of the event to be explained, that is we have not got an *explanandum* of the kind that Hempel and Oppenheim envisage. On the contrary, we have a specific causal claim. This is a neat way of making clear one of the differences between an explanation and a prediction; by showing the different kinds of proposition that they often are. When explaining Y, we do not have to be able to deduce that Y occurs, for we typically know this already. What we have to be able to deduce (if deduction is in any way appropriate) is that Y occurred *as a result of* a certain X, and of course this needs a very different kind of general law from the sort of general law that is required for prediction.

I shall now show that Scriven's treatment of such cases as post-explaining paresis on the basis of syphilis suffers from the same defect as his analysis of the evolutionary cases: *Insofar as there is an asymmetry, Scriven has failed to discern its precise locus, and having thus failed, he is led to suppose erroneously that Hempel's thesis is invalidated by such asymmetry as does obtain.*

Given a particular case of paresis as well as the proposition that the only cause of paresis is syphilis—where a "cause" is understood here with Scriven as a "contingently necessary condition"—what can be inferred?

---

[30] *Ibid.*, p. 480.

Scriven maintains correctly that what follows is that both the paretic concerned had syphilis and that, in his particular case, syphilis was the cause in the specified sense of "cause." And then Scriven goes on to maintain that his case against Hempel is established by the fact that we are able to assert that syphilis *did cause* paresis while *not* also being entitled to say that syphilis *will cause* paresis. But Scriven seems to have completely overlooked that our not being able to make both of these assertions does *not* at all suffice to discredit Hempel's thesis, which concerns the time-symmetry of the *inferability* of the *explanandum* from the *explanans*. The inadequacy of Scriven's argument becomes evident the moment one becomes aware of the *reason* for not being entitled to say that syphilis "will cause" paresis though being warranted in saying that it "did cause" paresis.

The sentences containing "did cause" and "will cause" respectively *each* make *two* affirmations as follows: (1) the assertion of the *explanandum* (paresis) *per se*; and (2) the affirmation of the obtaining of a causal *relation* (in the sense of being a contingently necessary condition) between the *explanans* (syphilis) and the *explanandum* (paresis). Thus, for our purposes, the statement "Syphilis *will cause* person Z to have paresis" should be made in the form "Person Z will have paresis *and* it will have been caused by syphilis"; and the statement "Syphilis *did cause* person K to have paresis" becomes "Person K has (or had) paresis *and* it was caused by syphilis." And the decisive point is that insofar as a *past* occurrence of paresis can be inductively *inferred from* prior syphilis, so also a future occurrence of paresis can be. For the causal relation or connection between syphilis and paresis is incontestably time-symmetric: precisely in the way and to the extent that syphilis *was* a necessary condition for paresis, it also *will* be! Hence the only *bona fide* asymmetry here is the record-based but innocuous one in the *assertibility* of the *explanandum* per se, but there is no asymmetry of *inferability* of paresis from syphilis. The former innocuous asymmetry is the one that interdicts our making the predictive assertion "will cause" while allowing us to make the corresponding post-explanatory assertion "did cause." And it is this fact which destroys the basis of Scriven's indictment of Hempel's thesis. For Hempel and Oppenheim did *not* maintain that an *explanandum* which can be post-asserted can *always* also be pre-asserted; what they did maintain was only that the *explanans* never post-explains any better or more conclusively than it implies predictively, there being complete symmetry between post-explanatory *inferability* and predictive *inferability* from a given *explanans*. They and Popper were therefore fully justified in testing the adequacy of a proffered *explanans* in the social sciences on the basis of whether the post-explanatory inferability of the *explanandum* which was claimed for it was matched by a corresponding predictive inferability, either inductive or deductive as the case may be.

What is the force of the following comment by Scriven: In the post-explanation of paresis we do not need to infer the *explanandum* from the *explanans* à la Hempel and Oppenheim, because we know this already from prior records (observations) of one kind or another; what we do need to infer instead is that the *explanandum*-event occurred *as a result of* the cause (necessary condition) given by the *explanans*, an inference which does *not* allow us to *predict* (i.e., pre-assert) the *explanandum*-event? This comment of Scriven's proves only that here there is record-based post-assertibility of paresis but no corresponding pre-assertibility.

In short, Scriven's invocation of the paresis case, just like his citation of the cases from evolutionary theory, founders on the fact that he has confused an *epistemological* asymmetry with a *logical* one. To this charge, Scriven has replied irrelevantly that he has been at great pains in his writings—as for example in his discussion of the barometer case which I shall discuss below—to distinguish valid arguments based on true premises which do qualify as scientific explanations from those which do not so qualify. This reply is irrelevant, since Scriven's *caveat* against identifying (confusing) arguments based on true premises which are both valid *and* explanatory with those which are valid without being explanatory does not at all show that he made the following crucial distinction here at issue: the distinction between (1) a difference (asymmetry) in the assertibility of either a conclusion (*explanandum*) or a premise (*explanans*); and (2) a difference (asymmetry) in the inferability of the *explanandum* from its *explanans*. Although the distinction which Scriven does make cannot serve to mitigate the confusion with which I have charged him, his distinction merits examination in its own right.

To deal with it, I shall first consider examples given by him which involve *non*-predictive valid deductive arguments to which he denies the status of being explanatory arguments. And I shall then conclude my refutation of Scriven's critique of Hempel's thesis by discussing the following paradigm case of his: the deductively valid *predictive* inference of a storm from a sudden barometric drop, which he adduces in an endeavor to show that such a valid deductive inference could not possibly qualify as a post-*explanation* of a storm.

It would be agreed on all sides, I take it, that no *scientific understanding* is afforded by the deduction of an *explanandum* from itself even though such a deduction is a species of valid inference. Hence it can surely be granted that the class of valid deductive arguments whose conclusion is an *explanandum* referring to some event or other is wider than the class of valid deductive arguments affording scientific understanding of the *explanandum* event. But it is a quite different matter to claim, as Scriven does, that no *scientific understanding* is provided by those valid deductive arguments which ordinary usage would not allow us to call "explanations." For example, Scriven cites the following case suggested by S. Bromberger and discussed by Hempel: the height of a flagpole is deducible from the length of its shadow and a measurement of the angle of the sun taken in conjunction with the principles of geometrical optics, but the height of the flagpole could not thereby be said to have been "explained."[31] Or take the case of a rectilinear triangle in physical space for which Euclidean geometry is presumed to hold, and let it be given that two of the angles are 37° and 59° respectively. Then it can be deductively inferred that the third angle is one of 84°, but according to Scriven, this would not constitute an explanation of the magnitude of the third angle.

Exactly what is shown by the flagpole and angle cases concerning the relation between valid deductive arguments which furnish scientific understanding and those which, according to ordinary usage, would qualify as "explanations"? I maintain that, while differing in one respect from what are usually called "explanations," the aforementioned valid deductive arguments yielding the height of the flagpole and the magnitude of the third angle provide scientific understanding no less than explanations do. And my reasons for this contention are the following.

In the flagpole case, for example, the *explanandum* (stating the height of the flagpole) can be deduced from two different kinds of premises: (1) an *explanans* of the type familiar from geometrical optics and involving laws of coexistence rather than laws of succession, antecedent events playing no role in the *explanans*; and (2) an *explanans* involving causally antecedent events and laws of succession and referring to the temporal genesis of the flagpole as an artifact. But is this difference between the

[31] Cf. C. G. Hempel, "Deductive-Nomological vs. Statistical Explanation," *op. cit.*, sec. 4.

kinds of premises from which the *explanandum* is deducible a basis for claiming that the coexistence-law type of *explanans* provides less *scientific understanding* than does the law-of-succession type of *explanans*? I reply: certainly not. And I hasten to point out that the difference between *pre-axiomatized* and axiomatized geometry conveys the measure of the scientific understanding provided by the *geometrical* account given in the flagpole and angle cases on the basis of laws of coexistence. But is it not true after all that ordinary usage countenances the use of the term "explanation" only in cases employing causal antecedents and laws of succession in the *explanans*? To this I say: this *terminological* fact is as unavailing here as it is philosophically unedifying.

Finally, we turn to Scriven's citation of cases of deductively valid predictive inferences which, in his view, invalidate Hempel's thesis because they could not possibly also qualify as post-explanations.

3. THE BAROMETER CASE

Scriven writes:

> What we are trying to provide when making a prediction is simply a claim that, at a certain time, an event or state of affairs will occur. In explanation we are looking for a cause, an event that not only occurred earlier but stands in a special relation to the other event. Roughly speaking, the prediction requires only a correlation, the explanation more. This difference has as one consequence the possibility of making predictions from indicators other than causes—for example, predicting a storm from a sudden drop in the barometric pressure. Clearly we could not say that the drop in pressure in our house caused the storm: it merely presaged it. So we can sometimes predict what we cannot explain.[32]

Other cases of the barometer type are cases such as the presaging of mumps by its symptoms and the presaging of a weather change by rheumatic pains.

When we make a predictive inference of a storm from a sudden barometric drop, we are inferring an effect of a particular cause from another (earlier) effect of that same cause. Hence the inference to the storm is *not* from a *cause* of the storm but only from an *indicator* of it.

[32] M. Scriven, "Explanation and Prediction in Evolutionary Theory," *op. cit.*, p. 480.

And the law connecting sudden barometric drops to storms is therefore a law affirming only an indicator type of connection rather than a causal connection.

The crux of the issue here is whether we have no scientific understanding of phenomena on the strength of their deductive inferability from indicator laws (in conjunction with a suitable antecedent condition), scientific understanding allegedly being provided only by an *explanans* making reference to one or more causes. If that were so, then Scriven could claim that although the mere *inferability* of particular storms from specific sudden barometric drops is admittedly time-symmetric, there is *no* time symmetry in *positive* scientific understanding. It is clear from the discussion of the flagpole case that the *terminological* practice of restricting the term "explanation" though *not* the term "prediction" to cases in which the *explanans* makes reference to a partial or total cause rather than to a mere indicator cannot settle the questions at issue, which are: Would the type of argument which yields a *prediction* of a future *explanandum* event (storm) from an indicator type of premise furnish any scientific understanding? And, if so, does this type of argument provide the same positive amount of scientific understanding of a corresponding *past* event (storm)?

These questions are, of course, *not* answered in the negative by pointing out correctly that the law connecting the cause of the storm with the storm can serve as a *reason* for the weaker indicator law. For this fact shows only that the causal law can account for both the storm and the indicator law, but it does not show that the indicator law cannot provide any scientific understanding of the occurrence of particular storms. To get at the heart of the matter, we must ask what distinguishes a causal law from an indicator law such that one might be led to claim, as Scriven does, that subsumption under indicator laws provides no scientific understanding at all, whereas subsumption under causal laws does.

Let it be noted that a causal law which is used in an *explanans* and is not itself derived from some wider causal law is fully as *logically contingent* as a mere indicator law which is likewise not derived from a causal law but is used as a premise for the deduction of an *explanandum* (either predictively or postdictively, i.e., H-explanatorily). Why then prefer (predictive or postdictive) subsumption of an *explanandum* under a causal law to subsumption under a mere indicator law? The justification for this preference would seem to lie not merely in the greater generality of the causal law; it also rests on the much larger variety of empirical contingencies which must be ruled out in the *ceteris paribus* clause specifying the relevant conditions under which the indicator law holds, as compared to the variety of such contingencies pertaining to the corresponding causal law. But this difference both in generality and in the variety of contingencies does not show that the indicator law provides no scientific understanding of particular phenomena subsumable under it; it shows only, so far as I can see, that one might significantly speak of *degrees* of scientific understanding. And this conclusion is entirely compatible with the contention required by the symmetry thesis that the barometric indicator law furnishes the same positive amount of scientific understanding of a past storm as of a future one predicted by it.

I believe to have shown, therefore, that with respect to the symmetry thesis, *Hempel ab omni naevo vindicatus.*[33]

IV

THE CONTROVERSY BETWEEN MECHANISM AND TELEOLOGY

The results of our discussion of the temporal asymmetry of recordability have a decisive bearing on the controversy between mechanism and teleology.

By mechanism we understand the philosophical thesis that all explanation must be *only a tergo*, i.e., that occurrences at a time t can be explained *only* by reference to *earlier* occurrences and *not also* by reference to later ones. And by teleology we understand a thesis which is the contrary rather than the contradictory of mechanism: all phenomena occurring at a time t (or, more narrowly, all phenomena belonging to a certain domain and occurring at a time t) are to be understood by reference to *later* occurrences only. We note that, thus understood, mechanism and teleology can *both* be false.

During our post-Newtonian epoch there is a misleading incongruity in using the term "mechanism" for the thesis of the monopoly of *a tergo* explanations. For in the context of the *time-symmetric* laws of Newton's mechanics, the given state of a closed mechanical stystem at a time t can

---

[33] Believing (incorrectly) to have cleansed Euclid of all blemish, G. Saccheri (1667-1733) published a book (Milan, 1733) under the title: *Euclides ab omni naevo vindicatus.*

be inferred from a state *later* than t (i.e., *retrodicted*) no less than the given state can be inferred from a state *earlier* than t (i.e., *predicted*). Instead of furnishing the prototype for mechanistic explanation in the philosophical sense, the phenomena described by the time-symmetric laws of Newton's mechanics constitute a domain with respect to which both mechanism and teleology are false, thereby making the controversy between them a *pseudo-issue*. More generally, that controversy is a pseudo-issue with respect to any domain of phenomena constituted by the evolution of closed systems obeying *time-symmetric* laws, be they deterministic or statistical.

But there is indeed a wide class of phenomena with respect to which mechanism is true. And one may presume that tacit reference to this particular class of phenomena has conferred plausibility on the thesis of the *unrestricted* validity of mechanism: traces or marks of interaction existing in a system which is essentially closed at a time t are accounted for scientifically by *earlier interactions* or *perturbations* of that system— which are called "causes"—and *not* by later interactions of the system.

In view of the demonstrated restricted validity of mechanism, we must therefore deem the following statement by H. Reichenbach as too strong: "We conclude: If we define the direction of time in the usual sense, there is no finality, and only causality is accepted as constituting explanation."[34]

[34] Reichenbach, *The Direction of Time, op. cit.*, p. 154.

Opening Statement

By Grunbaum

T HREE major ways in which temporal asymmetries enter into scientific induction are discussed as follows:

1. An account is given of the physical basis for the temporal asymmetry of recordability, which obtains in the following sense: except for humanly recorded predictions and one other class of advance indicators to be discussed, interacting systems can contain reliable indicators of only their *past* and *not* of their future interactions. To deal with the exceptional cases of non-spontaneous "pre-records," a clarification is offered of the essential differences in the conditions requisite to the *production* of an indicator having retrodictive significance ("post-record"), on the one hand, and of one having predictive significance ("pre-record" or recorded prediction), on the other. Purported counter-examples to the asymmetry of spontaneous recordability are refuted.

2. It is shown how in cases of asymmetric recordability, the associated retrodiction-prediction asymmetry makes for an asymmetry of *assertibility* as between an *explanandum* (or an *explanans*) referring to a future event and one referring to a past one. But it is argued that this *epistemological* asymmetry in the assertibility *per se* must be clearly distinguished from a *logical* asymmetry between the past and the future in regard to the *inferability* (deductive or inductive) of the *explanandum* from the *explanans*. And it is then contended that the failure to distinguish between an epistemological and a logical asymmetry vitiates the critiques that recent writers have offered of the Popper–Hempel thesis, which affirms symmetry of *inferability* as between predictive and post-explanatory *arguments*. In reply to Scriven, it is maintained that predictions based on mere indicators (rather than causes) do not establish an asymmetry in *scientific understanding* as between predictive arguments and post-explanatory ones.

3. As a further philosophical ramification of the retrodiction-prediction asymmetry, a set of sufficient conditions are stated for the correctness of philosophical mechanism as opposed to teleology.

Comments on Grünbaum Paper

By MICHAEL SCRIVEN

I

YOU remark that "an interaction itself is sufficient for its post-recording, but not for its pre-recording." I take this to be a conclusion based on physical arguments, and I note that it is incompatible with precognition. Hence, on the one hand your position is the basis for an interesting and novel argument against the possibility of precognition, and on the other hand it is vulnerable to the discovery, which has perhaps already been made, that precognition occurs.

II

Accepting for the moment your very clear account of the nature of Hempel-explanations and Hempel-predictions, we must now turn to the crucial question whether Hempel was engaged in analyzing the ordinary scientific concept of explanation, i.e., whether H-explanations and H-predictions were intended to be an analytical model of the ordinary scientific explanations and predictions. On this I would comment as follows:

A. There are two passages in the Hempel and Oppenheim paper where he makes it clear, or so it seemed to me, that he *is* interested in analyzing the usual scientific notions.

B. In a letter to me he has commented on certain rather incomplete-looking explanations unfavorably on the grounds that they would not be regarded as *scientifically* satisfactory, and this was said without any suggestion that an adequate defense of them would be provided if it were shown that they met the requirements of his model.

C. If Hempel was in fact giving an account of these special logical structures of his own, and they were not intended to be analyses of scientific explanation, then of course you and he would not be entitled to conclusions about the unsoundness or the scientifically unsatisfactory nature of what he calls "explanation sketches," which he regards as prevalent in the social sciences and history. There could be no objection to an explanation as unscientific on the grounds that it does not meet the conditions of the Hempelian model unless this model can be shown to be an analysis of ordinary satisfactory and scientific explanation.

Hence I conclude that Hempel not only did but had to attempt an analysis of the ordinary concept.

D. Now it is perfectly clear that there is no asymmetry between H-explanations and H-predictions. On the other hand it is equally clear that there is a gross asymmetry—in fact a whole series of asymmetries—between ordinary scientific explanations and predictions. It follows from the above considerations that this is a legitimate criticism of him. It is this kind of approach which his critics have taken and I cannot see that your comments are a successful defense of him unless some of the above points can also be repudiated.

E. Furthermore, I note that in your comments today you made a number of references to scientific understanding. It is very important to see that the H-explanations and H-predictions do not have to be in any way adequate to provide understanding. Mere subsumption under an unexplained and incomprehensible generalization does not provide us with understanding of the event which is thereby subsumed. But it does provide us with an H-explanation or an H-prediction. For this further reason there seems to be a failure of matching between the H-analysis and the actual object of analysis. We appear to get closer and closer to the point where we are setting out the properties of a peculiar formal object, which appears to have no interest at all; the only interest it could have at all would be if it were an analysis of scientific explanations and predictions. But as the divergencies between it and them grow, it becomes less and less interesting since it has no special interest of itself.

III

(This comment has been largely met by alterations made by Professor Grünbaum in the light of it.)

It seems to me that running through your remarks today there was some assumption that a cause is a sufficient condition for that of which it is a cause. This seems to me clearly false, and about as far from the mark as the H-explanations are from explanations. Contextual conditions apart, a cause is a non-redundant member of a set of conditions that are jointly sufficient for the effect. There is a peculiar sense in which it is sufficient— *given* the other conditions as fixed, then the addition of the cause is sufficient to bring about the effect. But it is not in an absolute sense sufficient. Similarly, and interestingly, there is a sense in which it is necessary—if it was absent then the remaining actual members of the jointly sufficient condition set are not by themselves enough to bring about the effect. But it is not itself a necessary condition for it might well be the case that there are six or seven other conditions which in conjunction with the remaining members of this set of jointly sufficient conditions would provide a sufficient set. There are various complicated reasons that account for the explanatory force of, and comprehension provided by giving a cause. These are not, I believe, in dispute. Now we turn to the syphilis case.[1] We are here able to go from the *that* of the explanation to the *why* of the explanandum just because we have an inference-license which guarantees to us that in each and every particular case where paresis occurs the cause—i.e., the explanation (in a suitable context)—is a prior infection with syphilis. There is thus no confusion between the *that* and the *why*, but a legitimate passage from one to the other.

IV

In summary then, there are cases where we are able to give the explanation of an event after it has occurred, whereas we could not possibly have predicted the occurrence of the event in advance; indeed we would have to—on the basis of excellent evidence—predict the *non*-occurrence of the event. Such a case is the paresis case and the case of murder by using a revolver[2] which I specified at the meeting. On the other hand, there are cases where prediction is possible in advance of the occurrence of an event, but explanation of its occurrence is not possible thereafter. For example: (1) Cows lying down in the field are a predictive indicator of rain, but could never be an explanation of the rain; (2) The fall of a barometer predicts but could not explain a storm. Here we have a reliable extrapolable correlation, which is not causally explanatory. Naturally it operates as a correlation only because some causes are kicking around somewhere; but it is not the indicator which causes the effect, and *hence* the prediction is possible when the explanation is not.

[1] See p. 136.
[2] Introduced in discussion; see p. 163.

VII

Mere Predictability

By Norwood Russell Hanson

T HAT explanation and prediction are logically symmetrical is a thesis much debated these past twenty years. Since Hempel hoisted this target critics have aimed to hit his account of explanation as inadequate. Within such areas as historical research, and even for some branches of science, explanations seem not always to be structured as Hempel suggests in his "covering law model"; they seem not to be logically symmetrical with a corresponding prediction.

I wish to shift the spotlight to Hempel's account of prediction. If he is right in stressing a symmetry between reasons supporting an explanation of *x* and reasons supporting a prediction of that same *x*, then we might have expected as much discussion of his account of prediction as has centered on his analysis of explanation.

I

My argument turns on a historical point. Contrast an eighteenth-century reaction to Newton's *Principia* with an early-twentieth-century reaction to that same theory. After 1687 Leibniz, and Poleni, were critical. To them *Principia* seemed *merely* a mathematical predicting device. Leibniz felt that this theory related to its observational data precisely as did Ptolemy's *Almagest* to *its* data. Ptolemy stressed that he could never hope to *explain* the wanderings of the planets. His aspiration was only to find a geometrical calculus through which he might forecast when next a given planet would halt in its eastward motion, "back up" a few degrees, and then continue forward again. Understanding beyond this exceeded Ptolemy's objectives. The *Almagest* was but a computational machine. It had some success in saying *when* celestial events might occur, but did not even undertake to ask *why* they occurred. Leibniz contended that the *Principia* had the same epistemic function vis-à-vis the data of mechanics. By providing a network of formulae, Newton enabled us to predict with precision the future motions of celestial bodies, the behavior of projectiles, the tides, etc. These predictions are anchored to the law of universal gravitation and the three laws of motion which bear Newton's name. Such laws structure a formal framework for generating numbers describing future events. But they are themselves neither explained nor explicable. Newton's sentiment is: "It is enough to have provided a formula by which mechanical behavior can be predicted. Beyond this, 'explaining' gravity, or space, or time, or inertia ... etc., does not concern me." For natural philosophers like Leibniz, however, such an attitude could not be reconciled with the idea of a complete science. Hence, throughout the early eighteenth century Newton's physics seemed only to predict—never to explain. It illustrated the "black box" conception of a scientific theory, of which we have heard so much. Feed the data numbers into the box, turn the handle (of the theory), and let the prediction numbers tumble out.

Contrast this view of Newton's mechanics with the one current in the nineteenth century—as encapsulated in C. D. Broad's book of 1913, *Perception, Physics, and Reality*. Broad described Newton's laws as constituting the paradigms of causal *explanation*. After demonstrating a formal connection between mechanical phenomena and these laws, no further *understanding* was required, since this very demonstration constituted the most complete explanation possible.

In two centuries, therefore, a change of philosophical importance had occurred. Yet the theory in question, Newton's mechanics, remained essentially the same. The refinements of Laplace, Lagrange, Maxwell, and Hertz did not affect the formal structure of the theory, although they did make it function more smoothly as a piece of inferential machinery.

But now, since the theory was identically structured at both times, Hempel's thesis, if correct, should obtain with equal force in either context. Whatever counted as a prediction of x in the eighteenth century should then have been logically symmetrical with some corresponding explanation of x: what counted as a prediction of x in the twentieth century should also be symmetrical with a corresponding explanation. But the conceptual difference between Leibniz and Broad is not illuminated by Hempel's analysis. Leibniz would have characterized Newton's mechanics as grinding out a *mere* prediction of x, in the total absence of a corresponding explanation. Broad felt no such reservation: the same network of inferences which failed to convey understanding of mechanical phenomena to Leibniz constituted (for Broad) everything "under-standing mechanical phenomena" could mean. Since Hempel is concerned only with networks of inference per se, his account cannot resolve this historical paradox.

Our purpose is to explore the notion of *mere* predictability. This may help us analyze the attitudes of Leibniz and Broad and also to discover where Hempel's thesis really obtains. What counts as *mere* predictability (i.e., numerical forecasting) at one time may serve as full-blown pre-diction (i.e., advance *explanation* of future events) at another time. Hempel cannot distinguish the two. Hence he has been attacked for appearing to give an account of the latter, when perhaps his thesis has concerned the former.

II

Let's think ourselves back into the heyday of optimism for classical mechanics. This would be about 1847—just after Leverrier's brilliant pre-diction of the existence of Neptune by an extrapolation of the explanatory techniques of Newton's *Principia*. This triumph raised the theory to the highest pinnacle it ever had, or ever has, known. One or two minor local flaws marred the complete victory of the theory.

Imagine that at such a time a young mathematician—let us call him "Notwen"—comes forward with "an alternative to Newton's theory," invoked initially just to deal with those minor flaws. The alternative is algebraically complex. To use Notwenian theory at all requires skill in unfamiliar branches of functional analysis. Moreover, the fundamental postulates of Notwen's theory are replete with uninterpreted terms like $\sqrt{-1}$, "negative velocities," "infinite densities," etc. But suppose also that this new theory, then in 1847, turned out results identical to what orthodox Newtonian mechanics could then achieve, as well as coping with those minor flaws which started Notwen working on his theory in the first place. (This is the first stage in our thought experiment.)

In short, when first announced, the new and unfamiliar Notwenian theory generates all the predictions and all the numbers that ordinary Newtonian theory can generate, and also patches up some minor flaws. What, then, would be the standard attitude toward this "alternative"? I submit that it would be regarded as a mathematical curiosity, with con-siderable puzzlement concerning how and why it works at all. It would be described as a mere predicting device—an intra-mathematical analogue of a mysteriously complex machine which, as if by numerological magic, seems to bring forth the correct answer to all questions. In such a context no one would try to *explain* phenomena by appeal to Notwen's system.

Suppose further that orthodox Newtonian mechanics begins to show major weaknesses. Problems it cannot solve, and events it cannot predict, turn up with increasing frequency—while at the same time Notwen's theory, by simple extension, succeeds with such new problems and events with remarkable precision. This alone will decide nothing. But scientists will begin to show increasing reliance on the new "alternative to Newton." Courses dealing with the newer mathematical techniques necessary within Notwenian mechanics will come to be taught in the better universities. The "old guard" will insist that the Notwen theory gains its accuracy 'by accident"—and explains nothing. But the energies of younger, physicists will turn more and more to the internal development of Notwenian physics. (This is the second stage in our imaginary example.)

Suppose, finally, that as Newtonian mechanics continues to fall apart. Notwenian physics opens up new branches of science, focuses on problems never before perceived, fuses disciplines thought before to be distinct, and sharpens experimental techniques to an unprecedented degree. Imagine the whole scientific enterprise caught up within the basic metabolism of Notwenian physics. The very pattern of thinking within any inquiry properly called "scientific" will reflect that of the new physics— by now become virtually synonymous with the concepts of "science" and "scientific explanation." To have become able to cope with a scientific problem at all will be just to have become able to build it into the conceptual framework of the Notwenian physics. (This is the third stage in our *gedankenexperiment*.)

Consider these three stages more schematically:

1. First comes the presentation of an algorithmic novelty. E.g., some intricate piece of formalism is introduced which, miraculously, churns out all the observational consequences of some older and more familiar theory, as well as patching up some minor flaws in the latter. This is what is sometimes called a "black box" theory. No deep understanding about phenomena follows merely from the successful use of the algorithm. Still, scientists seem prepared to use the new technique on trial because of its capacity to get numerical results. Then they translate these results into

more familiar terms of the orthodox theory in order to provide *understanding*.

2. The next stage consists in the new formalism beginning to outstrip the extant theory with respect to "predictive power." Although affording no more "insight" into the phenomena than before, the new theory appears now not simply as a remarkable algebraic alternative to the orthodox theory; it has now become essential for getting numbers at the predictional-observational level. It will have ceased being merely a "black box"—it is now a "gray box." It is still opaque so far as providing understanding of phenomena goes. But now it appears that there must be some fundamental reason why the new formalism works in predictions where the old theory has collapsed. The new theory is no longer viewed as merely mathematical magic; it now seems that its structure and that of the phenomena with which it deals must have something in common. Otherwise it could not be succeeding where the older, more familiar theory has failed.

3. At this stage, the new theory will have pushed into fields far from the minor phenomena with which it began. It will connect subject matters formerly thought distinct. The new theory will have so permeated the operations and techniques of the body of science that its structure will appear to be *the* pattern of a scientific inquiry. At this stage it will seem a "glass box." Because of the pervasive patterns of reasoning which the new theory establishes within so many related disciplines, scientists will cease distinguishing between *its* structure and that of the "phenomena themselves". The equations of the new theory will seem actually to mirror the processes of nature; the presuppositions of the theory will constitute fountainheads of understanding for everything flowing from those suppositions. And indeed, what else *can* one think about phenomena other than what the currently most successful physical theory permits? In short, the theory will have become known by its fruits—its capacity to provide understanding will have grown in direct ratio to its capacity to generate successful predictions within increasingly wider areas of inquiry. And our very idea of what "understanding" means will have grown, and changed, with the growth and changes of the theory. So also with our idea of "explanation."

These three stages characterize the development of classical mechanics itself. When Newton enunciated his "mathematical philosophy," there were several prose-laden theories of nature already in the field: e.g., the theory of impetus, Kepler's celestial "spokes of force," Cartesian Vortex mechanics, etc. These theories purported to make phenomena intelligible, by relating them to intuitively evident first principles, in a manner which Newton's contemporaries felt he had not achieved. Thus Leibniz' attack on Newton's mechanics is a Stage-One assault. It is much like what would have been a typical reaction to Notwenian mechanics in 1847. Broad's adulation is typical of Stage Three; by 1900 the Newtonian pattern of thinking had permeated every corner of the house of science. The place that Newtonian first principles occupied within an immense pattern of interlocking analyses and types of inquiry made it seem like a glass-box theory when C. D. Broad wrote. In a profound sense the theory seemed to provide a glimpse of the innermost workings of nature itself. It was as if '$F \propto \gamma(Mm/r^2)$' in some way *pictured* something in nature, as in some sense it may. But in Leibniz' time, these extensive and manifold ramifications of the theory in other extra-mechanical disciplines were absent. Hence it was construed as being merely a "black box."

It is tempting to characterize the theory of quantum mechanics as already well advanced in its second phase—its gray-box stage. For many years it has been providing answers to questions about microphysical nature which Newtonian theory was incapable of doing. Moreover, it seems no longer to be regarded as merely constituting the mathematical conjury which dominated the period between 1913 and 1927. Still, it has not yet permeated enough into related fields, e.g., theoretical chemistry, genetics, to make many insist that it constitutes a paradigm of scientific explanation. On the contrary, many philosophers mark deficiencies in the explanatory framework of quantum mechanics. This may signal only a delayed Stage-One reaction, or it may reflect the fact that the Stage-Two successes of quantum mechanics have not been as spectacular as were those of Newtonian mechanics in the late eighteenth and early nineteenth centuries.

In any case, that Leibniz didn't, while Broad did, feel Newtonian mechanics to constitute the best of all possible explanations of nature, reflects a clear conceptual difference between them. This difference is not ust a function of *internal* changes within the theory: the basic inferential patterns of classical mechanics have undergone no *substantial* modifications from the seventeenth century up to the present time. The difference between them, however, may be a function of differences between the degree to which Newtonian mechanics had permeated and interlocked every scientific discipline by 1900, as contrasted with the relative absence of any such systematic and synoptic effect in the *Principia* in 1700—at least so far as disciplines outside of mechanics (strictly interpreted) are concerned. The wider conceptual "set" of a physical theory is not merely a matter of psychological importance. It affects our understanding of the conceptual status of a given theory, of its logical relationship to other theories and to observations—and to our ideas concerning what it is to *understand* something, or to *explain* it. Just as we know something about an animate object when we see how its insides function, so we know more about it when we also see how *it* functions in relation to other organisms, of the same kind, and of different kinds. With physical theories it is much the same. When born, they are subjected to minute microanalysis. But at this stage it is rarely clear what they may ultimately be able to *do*. When what they can do becomes known, even some of the earlier microanalysis may change. Leibniz had little knowledge of how much the *Principia* was going to be able to do. Broad did. Their different attitudes toward its powers to explain are a reflection of this difference.

Hempel's account of the logical symmetry between explanation and prediction is sound as a piece of formal syntactical analysis. The logical structure of theories is such that for every well-made prediction there will be some correspondingly well-made postdiction.[1] This is as true of every well-made seventeenth-century prediction as it is of every well-made twentieth-century prediction. However, not every postdiction will count at *all* times as an explanation. A postdiction embedded in a far-flung system of scientific theories *may* count as an explanation. At another time, however, the *same* pattern of inference, the same postdiction, may constitute nothing of the kind.

By 1913 Newton's postdictions had become explanations: Newtonian theory had become a glass box. "Backward inferences" within the theory i.e., inferences from present or past events to their known initial conditions, seemed like backward glances at nature's inner workings. For

---

[1] By a postdiction I mean simply the logical reversal of a prediction. If a prediction consists in working from initial conditions through boundary conditions to a statement about some future event x, then a postdiction will consist in inferring from a statement about some present event x, through the boundary conditions, back to not generally unique initial conditions. Every prediction, if inferentially respectable, must possess a corresponding postdiction. This is part of Hempel's thesis, and it is sound.

Leibniz, however, the postdictions were *merely* postdictions. They were simply arguments reversed along the time parameter. The theory was a black box. Backward inferences were for Leibniz no more than the consideration back-to-front of a sequence of mathematical moves involving t. Predictions in the *Principia*, therefore, were *mere* predictions for Leibniz; they were logically symmetrical only with postdictions. For Broad, predictions within Newtonian theory were mature; they *were* logically symmetrical with explanations—i.e., postdictions seen now as parts of an immense interlocking pattern of related hypotheses, inferences, and observational data. Hempel's analysis per se cannot distinguish these two cases— cannot distinguish prediction from *mere* prediction. But the entire history of science is representable as a relentless advance from *mere* prediction to prediction; this, just as much as it is an advance from postdiction to explanation. Both prediction and explanation are concepts reflecting networks and patterns of theories: postdiction and *mere* prediction reflect only the internal structure and direction of particular inferences in particular sciences. By generalizing a logical truth of the latter kind, Hempel may have misled us concerning a conceptual issue of the former kind.

Mr. Hanson was unable to attend the conference; there was therefore no occasion for him to summarize his paper. Ed.

Comments on Grünbaum and Hanson Papers

By ROBERT S. COHEN

I

SINCE I have no essential disagreement with Grünbaum's essay, I shall confine my comments to his philosophical method. This is all the more appropriate because the systematic relation between empirical science and philosophical understanding is still a disputed one. Grünbaum properly uses physics in philosophical discussion. In the present essay, thermodynamic discussions about the interactions of open or quasi-closed systems are not just relevant *illustrations*; rather, they are relevant *arguments* (or *reasons*). They must be discussed scientifically, or in terms of the philosophical relevance which is alleged to exist.

Grünbaum wishes to explain an apparent situation wherein retrodiction is possible or relatively assured, while prediction is either impossible or relatively unsure. An account of this is sought from the empirical science of statistical thermodynamics. This is so, of course, because this branch of physics is concerned with the energy states of systems and their transformations and interactions, and because it has provided theorems about entropy which have been used to investigate temporal order and other properties of time. There may seem to be no difficulty with this straightforward procedure, but Grünbaum, at least, is prepared to pay any hidden price of accepting counter-intuitive surprise where, and if, necessary. Thus we can seriously consider time reversal for certain natural processes. Part of Grünbaum's way of philosophizing may be termed the use and analysis of scientific, that is, extraordinary language. Why reject ordinary language analysis, as in Scriven's comparison of prediction-by-correlation with explanation-by-causal-theory, in such scientific matters as these? Because they *require* analyses of logical relations between an explanandum and an explanans, whether simple generalizations or complex formulation of theory, and they may also demand exposition of restricted parts of statistical mechanics and its empirical data. This method of scientific philosophizing is not new, but it is often neglected, whether by choice, oversight, or lack of sufficient means to cope with all the possibly relevant empirical science. It is not only that one should simply not say what is not so, as Professor Black remarked at an earlier session, but that one must oneself think through the very interaction of disciplines which such a conference as this seeks to encourage among scholars. Grünbaum does this.

There are disagreements at the physical level itself, and relevant physical arguments are not to be taken on authority. Even the analysis of interactions of quasi-closed branch systems is not so well established as to be beyond debate. Thus, Mehlberg recently criticized the branch-system hypothesis and the view that natural time is anisotropic, and Grünbaum's reply will be anticipated with interest.[1]

II

It may seem that we are concerned, in this session, with a spectrum of types of explanation: empirical theories, deductive systems, correlations. We are not, I think, concerned with mere forecasts. Grünbaum and Hanson discuss varieties of inductive inference, conceived as the passage from singular to universally applicable statements, or in general as the passage from present knowledge to knowledge of what is not-present. The latter may be the unknown future, the unknown present (which is elsewhere or even right here), the unknown past; or there may be layers of inference, as when we infer from such a record as a footprint or a memory that there was an occurrence, our explanandum, and then we proceed to establish an explanation as best we can, our explanans, which itself requires inductive establishment and deductive elaboration. The asymmetry of time in our epoch of the universe, as presently understood, provokes an asymmetry in scientific explanation only because there is this primary factual inference to the explanandum for a past interaction whereas there is no corresponding inference either to or from a future interaction.

Here we wonder whether Grünbaum considers memories to be primary records of the same thermodynamic and epistemological functions as other systematic interactions.

We may assert that an inference to the future establishes an explanandum only conditionally (for further explanation or prediction by other inferential paths), and that this is *no more* doubtful an inference than one to the past via a presently persisting subjective memory or objective record, which are, after all, mere inferential base points. Nevertheless the symmetry is spurious, for the presently observed record provides an inference which rests on the overwhelmingly confirmed principles of statistical thermodynamics of incompletely isolated systems. And if *this* scientific asymmetry is not sufficiently important to some philosophers, at any rate, it seems to be the only asymmetry in the situation.

[1] Henry Mehlberg, "Physical Laws and Time's Arrow," *Current Issues in the Philosophy of Science*, H. Feigl and G. Maxwell, editors, New York, 1961.

III

Concerning a conditional explanandum, we can restate one of Scriven's examples as follows: If paresis, then prior syphilis. And this is time-symmetric, equally valid in the future or the past.

IV

Hanson adopts the instrumentalist view (as Popper and others have called it) of theories in their early stages, or of any theoretical schemes of a correlational or computational sort. But Hanson gives no reason to adopt the view attributed to Broad that a theory which has become complex and synoptic (i.e., successful) has thereby become an explanation while itself earlier was a mere instrument. We do not know why Hanson thinks that Leibniz and Broad were both right. He seems to be about to offer what we would welcome from a scholar of his philosophical and historical insights: an explanation of the history of the idea of scientific explanation, but such an explanation should, one supposes, be historical or sociological. Yet he claims logical import for such historical changes in the philosophical and scientific evaluations of a theory. And what is the import? All we seem to have is a distinction between a theory-in-itself and a theory-as-matured, that is as developed and applied to a network of logically surrounding theories. I would rather have thought that, if we assume Hanson to be correct in his description of the eighteenth century critique of Newton, Leibniz was wrong then, or Broad was wrong fifty years ago; and that Hanson can tell us which and why.

Reply to Cohen

By Grünbaum

In so far as Mehlberg's denial of the aniosotropy of time concerns the contents of my essay in this volume, I have already given my reply to Mehlberg's thesis of temporal isotropy in footnote 6 of section II of my paper. And I must therefore point out that Professor Cohen misleads the reader by saying that my reply to Mehlberg is being "anticipated" with interest, although I appreciate that Professor Cohen was probably referring to my forthcoming reply to *other* facets of Mehlberg's thesis.

In view of the fact that Mr. Scriven's comments on Mr. Grünbaum's paper were communicated to Mr. Grünbaum prior to the conference, and that Mr. Grünbaum took account of these objections and replied to them in the body of his paper, Mr. Grünbaum has agreed that there is no need for a separate reply to Mr. Scriven's remarks. Ed.

Reply to Cohen
By HANSON

PROFESSOR COHEN's comments on "*Mere* Prediction" are terse and trenchant. But he misunderstood me. I did not myself purport to give criteria in virtue of which Newton's mechanical theory was a mere calculus in the seventeenth century while it was a genuine explanation in the early twentieth. My inquiry was occasioned by a simple historical fact: Leibniz *did* regard the *Principia* as a physically uninterpretable calculus. Broad regarded the same work as constituting a paradigm of scientific explanation. These contentions are, of course, documentable.

Cohen challenges me to say which of them, Leibniz or Broad, is correct; he takes it for granted that they cannot both be correct. Yet it was my intention to raise doubts about questions of the Cohen type. *What counts* as an explanation of phenomena at any time may not be a function simply of the inferential equipment provided by a theoretical structure. Given essentially the same theoretical structure, i.e., Newton's *Principia* considered in the seventeenth century and in the twentieth, this may at one time strike scientists as being a mere calculus, and at another time seem to offer complete explanation. This is what happened. Nor must illumination of this historical fact be "a mere prose poem"—as some of my "universally quantified" colleagues insist. For this fact has *conceptual* consequences. Our understanding of what an explanation *is* will be affected by the fact that a given inferential structure will at one time serve to explain phenomena while at another time it will not.

This is so obvious within recent physics that it is strange for an accomplished physicist-philosopher like Professor Cohen to be other than sympathetic. Consider the impossibility of characterizing the "state" of an electron in anything like classical, Hamiltonian terms. The noncommutativity of the position and momentum operators within any workable version of quantum theory provides another instance—the result being that we cannot even *describe* a microparticle in terms suited to the nineteenth- and early twentieth-century fiction, the punctiform mass. Consider further how, in a laboratory, we can excite an H-atom's electron so that it moves from an inner orbit to an outer orbit; yet we do not even possess the idea of that particle having had any physical existence *between* those two orbits. These features are built into the algorithm within which quantum-theoretical reasoning takes place. But must it not also be admitted that the conceptual resistance to these features of microphysics is very slight amongst working physicists today? And must we not also admit that, amongst working physicists of the 1928–1935 period, the resistance to such features of particle physics was considerably greater?

What our physics professors, in their student days, regarded as limitations of the new quantum mechanics—these are no longer felt to be limitations in any conceptually significant sense. Not by the majority. Now it is this developmental fact, and this alone, which it was my purpose to set out. What *counts* as an explanation among most physicists now would not have counted as an explanation during the 1928–1935 period. What counted as an explanation for Broad in the early twentieth century did not count as an explanation in the late seventeenth and early eighteenth centuries. And yet, in both cases, the formal features of the inferences concerned remained essentially unaltered. The conclusion? The anatomy of "explanation" and of "prediction," as these terms are widely understood, may not be revealed by probings and explorations of the "symbolic logic" kind. For these concepts gain much of their content, at any time, from the wider scientific context within which particular scientific formalisms are used, and related to other more familiar theoretical techniques.

The contrast between "mere prediction" and "mere postdiction" is a structural feature of any given scientific theory. Explicating *this* relationship is explicating the formal properties of the theory itself. Moreover, this relationship remains constant, so long as the logic of the theory remains constant—all the way from the seventeenth century to the twentieth century within classical mechanics, and all the way from the 1928–1935 period to the present day within quantum mechanics. But the richer conceptual content of the contrast between prediction and explanation changes in time, and through the history of science. And it is this contrast which needs more discussion by scholars concerned with the conceptual content of what *scientists* call "explanations" and "predictions."

Discussion on Grünbaum and Hanson Paper

(Based on notes taken by EDWARD MADDEN and MYRON ANDERSON)

SCRIVEN: Here are some examples which serve to show the lack of symmetry between prediction and explanation:

1. If a man has paresis, we can explain the fact that he has paresis by referring to the fact that he had syphilis prior to the paresis. This is an explanation, because syphilis *causes* paresis; but we would not be able to *predict* paresis from a knowledge that the man had syphilis, because paresis does not invariably follow syphilis.

2. We place in front of a man a hundred automatics. One of them is loaded. At the other end of the room we place another man. The first man is to close his eyes, spin around, pick up one of the guns, point it at the other man, and pull the trigger. We ask the observers to predict whether there will shortly be a death in the room, supposing that the first man never misses. Since only one of the guns is loaded, it is perfectly clear that the prediction must be: "There will not be a death." Now the first man picks up a gun and shoots the second man. Someone comes into the room, sees the dead body, and asks how the man died. We *explain* his death by saying that the first man shot him. That is, we use as an explanation the very fact that we were willing to predict would not occur.

3. We can have a perfectly good deductive relationship without explanation: Given statements about the length of the shadow of a flagpole, and the angle at which light is falling on it, we can infer the height of the flagpole. But clearly the height of the flagpole is not explained thereby.

4. We can even have prediction without explanation: Suppose that cows invariably lie down before rain, so that from the fact that cows lie down, we can invariably correctly predict that rain will occur. But we would certainly not claim that the fact that the cows lie down explains the occurrence of rain.

GRÜNBAUM: In the case of the flagpole we must distinguish between genetic explanation of the flagpole's height which is not provided by statements about the length of its shadow, and the type of understanding provided by statements which place the flagpole's height in the context of geometrical optics. If this latter type is not accepted, then coexistence laws provide us with no explanation. However, Scriven is correct in insisting that a deductive relationship is not always an explanatory one.

In the case of indicators (such as the behavior of the cows) these do provide explanation, though in an attentuated fashion requiring a context of wider information before we would use the term "explain" in its more conventional sense.

MORGENBESSER: In the social sciences there is certainly an assymmetry between prediction and explanation. On Hempel's scheme we must at the least have lawlike statements to serve as premises in our deductions; so even to approach his ideal in the social sciences would require an analysis of what a lawlike statement is. Whether every explanation in the social sciences needs to be based on a lawlike statement is still another question. I think it is possible to formulate criteria for explanation in the social sciences which are quite different from those that Hempel would insist upon, and which would not be at all applicable to predictions.

BRAITHWAITE: I should like to register a strong objection to Hanson's "black box" metaphor. We don't know what goes on inside a black box, by definition; but in the case of a deductive physical theory, the scientist knows precisely what goes on "inside" his calculus. The calculus is not a black box at all.

I should say that explanation has degrees. The more useful a system—i.e., the wider its scope—the greater the degree of explanation or understanding it affords when it is applied to a particular case.

SCRIVEN: I don't think there is really such a great difference between Hanson and Braithwaite. Hanson's metaphor of the black box is intended to suggest that, so far as the calculus alone is concerned, we may have *mere* predictability; but when we have a wider deductive system, the box becomes transparent, we can see what is going on inside it, and we have *real* predictability.

MORGENBESSER: Wouldn't you say, Mr. Braithwaite, that we do have many cases where some scientists, at any rate, refuse to accept certain things as giving us a real picture of nature, even though the theory was used very successfully for prediction? I refer again to the classical case of action at a distance.

BRAITHWAITE: I should say that protests that "this isn't an explanation" were due to the fact that it was contrary to the person's prejudices.

MORGENBESSER: Well, call it prejudice if you will, but I think that very frequently it is simply that the theories don't jibe with the way they expect nature to be; and in this respect we have to judge from our own point of view concerning the way we expect nature to be. Look at the disputes concerning extrasensory perception. But successful predictions by means of the theory may alter these general beliefs.

BLACK: I should like to protest mildly against Mr. Braithwaite's assumption that the only alternative to the approach he defended so ably in his book is something like Weber's *Verstehen*. The notion of understanding is not all that mysterious that one may ask in a tone of outrage, "What's understanding?" In the past, many great scientists have recognized the difference between mere predictability and explanatory power. Only a naïve positivism would deny that there is something to be recognized here. And while positivism is a point of view, it is not the only point of view, and it is not an exclusive competitor to Weber.

SELLARS: I think that the discussion between Grünbaum and Scriven was interesting and important, but marred by terminological differences and a failure to make relevant distinctions. In the flagpole case we are not giving an explanation in any ordinary sense of the fact that the flagpole is x' high. The flagpole case does involve, however, an understanding of the relationship between height and length of shadow. We must distinguish between (a) explaining a particular matter of fact, (b) explaining *how we know* a particular matter of fact by showing that it falls under an applicable generalization to which we are scientifically entitled, (c) explaining *how we know* that this generalization obtains (e.g., simple induction, theoretical reasoning), and (d) explaining the generalization itself. Compare the flagpole case with that of the cows and rain. In neither case is the particular matter of fact explained—neither the fact that the flagpole is x' high, nor the fact that it will rain. In both cases we are able to explain *how we know* that the particular matter of fact obtains. In both cases we are able to explain *how we know* that the relevant generalization obtains. In the flagpole case but not in the cow case we can explain the generalization itself. This is why we are tempted to say that in the flagpole case the fact that the flagpole is x' high has been explained.

BERLYNE: There are certainly differences between explanation and prediction as forms of behavior. The circumstances in which one would like to know what will happen and the circumstances in which one would like to know why something happened are not the same. They involve different motivational conditions, and a formula that satisfies somebody looking for an explanation will not necessarily satisfy somebody looking for a prediction or vice versa.

There are, moreover, great individual differences in the kinds of situation that make people seek explanations and the kinds of formula that will lead them to feel that they have successfully completed the search. The corresponding variation is appreciably smaller in the case of prediction. These individual differences have been responsible for some of the disputes among scientists. They are well illustrated by some of the controversies in psychology. At one extreme, we have psychologists like Skinner who are content as long as they know the factors that will make a particular kind of behavior more likely and thus enable them to control its occurrence. At the other extreme, we have the view favored by the "understanding" psychologists who flourished in Germany in the early years of the present century and who believed that a psychologist must aim at a kind of emotional, intuitive, even artistic understanding of behavior.

MORGENBESSER: Explanation involves putting an event into one's general world picture. This applies both to children and to psychologists.

BLACK: I dug out from Cohen's remarks the phrase, "The use and analysis of extraordinary (scientific) language." Grünbaum is quite deliberately not analyzing ordinary discourse, but is introducing new and extra-ordinary language. That is his privilege, as long as we know (and he knows) what he is doing. Hempel's and Grünbaum's form of philo-sophizing in their analysis of explanation is an example of what I should like to call "unbridled reconstructionism." But I would argue that they are not analyzing the concept of explanation; they are analyzing the concept of inference. Obviously there is time symmetry in inference; but this fact is trivial, since inference is timeless.

I should say that the request for a bare explanation of x is as in-complete as the question, "Is Mr. Braithwaite near?" Explanation is a relative concept, and requires supplementation by a preamble. If you will say that such-and-such is puzzling, discrepant, or what have you, whereas *this* ... then you begin to have a context in which you know what you are looking for.

In introducing extraordinary language, as Hempel is doing in his "analysis" of explanation, one is really giving a persuasive definition. The geometric ideal of Euclid is being presented (by outsiders) as the model to which science ought to conform to be respectable; this is a very dubious theory. One can wholeheartedly subscribe to the value of deductive procedures where they work, without supposing that this is a supreme maxim of science.

BAR-HILLEL: "Explanation" and "prediction" as usually used are prag-matic terms. Hempel, in trying to reconstruct the concept, has found that the only semantical relationship worth abstracting from these prag-matic notions is that of inference, or deducibility. Because of this it is easy to find counter-examples to Hempel's thesis in ordinary usage. Pragmatically, explanation and prediction are not at all symmetrical

For example, in the ordinary sense of the terms, one is responsible for predictions, but not in the same sense responsible for explanations. There is an enormous pragmatic distinction.

FINCH: Are we not responsible in some cases for explaining the past?

BAR-HILLEL: Only indirectly.

MORGENBESSER: Hempel's model of explanation is not only clear, but in its insistence upon there. being a law statement in the explanans, provides for the removal of puzzlement by showing that events are not idiosyncratic. Removing idiosyncracy helps remove puzzlement, and in so far as this is the aim of explanation, Hempel's model satisfies it.

BLACK: I almost entirely agree with Bar-Hillel; I just want to suggest that he is too pessimistic about the possibilities of becoming clear about the ordinary notion of explanation, once one specifies the "preamble" involved.

GRÜNBAUM: I agree that the flagpole example is not explanation if one is taking a pragmatic point of view. But the analysis of the inferential element in the explanation of the height of the flagpole is not trivial …

BLACK: I never claimed that the analysis of the inference was trivial. What is trivial is this: offering an analysis of the concept of inference as an analysis of the concept of explanation.

GRÜNBAUM: And furthermore, in the matter of inference, I am not in the least committed to the *deductive* model.

SCRIVEN: The difference between explanation and prediction is not pragmatic, but can be drawn on semantical lines, as my example of the revolver shows. There is no pragmatic element in the explanation here.

SCRIVEN (comment arising from a discussion with Bar-Hillel; submitted after the meeting): There is a certain formal peculiarity about asymmetrical explanations which is worth pointing out. Suppose for the moment we include the justification of an explanation or a prediction in the explanation or prediction, as Hempel does. From a general law and antecedent conditions we are then entitled to deduce that a certain event will occur in the future. This is the deduction of a prediction. From one of the propositions of the form, "The only possible cause of y is x," and a statement that y has occurred we are able to deduce, not only that x must have occurred, but also the proposition, "The cause of y in this instance was x." I take this to be a perfectly sound example of deducing and explanation. Notice, however, that what we have deduced is not at all a description of the event to be explained; that is, we have not got an explanandum of the kind that Hempel and Oppenheim envisage. On the contrary, we have a specific causal claim. This is a neat way of making clear one of the differences between an explanation and a prediction; by showing the different kinds of proposition that they often are. When explaining y, we do not have to be able to deduce that y occurs, for we typically know this already. What we have to be able to deduce (if deduction is in any way appropriate) is that y occurred *as a result of* a certain x, and of course this needs a very different kind of general "law" from the sort of general law that is required for prediction.

VIII

The Deductive Model and its Qualifications

By Sidney Morgenbesser

The deductive model of a satisfactory explanation, once a weapon against the idealist right, has recently become a target for criticisms, especially from the ordinary left. Some of these criticisms are wild; others, better directed, damage the model. None destroy it. The model, therefore, remains intact but in need of minor repairs, some of which I hope will be indicated in this paper, which aims at a defense of a qualified version of the model; especially against those critics who claim its non-applicability to the social sciences in general and history in particular.

Some critics claim that the deductive model is intended as an analysis of such phrases as "is an explanation of" or "explains," etc. But this claim is wild, for there are many deductive models, not only one. The criteria offered by Professor Nagel for a satisfactory deductive explanation of a law differ from those offered by Professor Hempel, for example. More-over, all of these models aim to be not a general explication of "is an explanation of," but only a specification of the necessary and sufficient conditions for the true application of "is a deductive explanation of J," where "J" stands in place of a name, description of an event, or law.

To discuss all these deductive models would require not a paper but a seminar. Hence, in what follows, I shall restrict my attention to a review of the restricted deductive model, which attempts to explicate "is a deductive explanation of E" where "E" stands in place of a name or description of an event. Fortunately the refined versions of this model, offered by Professor Nagel and Professor Hempel, differ but slightly, and we can assume familiarity with both of them. Of course, the general point behind the model that an event is explained if and only if it is covered by law is an ancient one, and no one in our generation should claim credit for its discovery.

Note, however, the difference to which we have already alluded: The tradition discusses the explanation of an event, the restricted deductive model, the deductive explanation of one. Without this difference the deductive model becomes identical with the covering-law model and is subject to the criticism that there are many acceptable non-deductive explanations. The instruction is important, for it is occasionally overlooked that the conditions specified by the restricted deductive model for a deductive explanation of an event are used by the covering law as conditions for the explanation of one, and that hence the deductive model is entailed by but not equivalent to the covering-law one. On occasion, it is also forgotten that the restricted deductive model specifies not a necessary and sufficient condition of the explanation of an event, but only a sufficient one. But here expansion is required in order to forestall obvious criticism.

It is well known that it is misleading to discuss the explanation of an event. The reasons are patent. Since there are descriptions without end that apply to any event, it is not obvious that we can sensibly attempt to explain an event; since an event can be explained under one description and not another one, it is not apparent which explanation counts as *the* explanation of the event. Thus our previous remarks require expansion, but not necessarily revision. I suggest that we discuss not the explanation of an event, but the explanation of an event under a given description of it; and that we read "is an explanation of E" as short for "is an explanation of E under K" where "K" stands in place of the statement deduced from the explanans. Of course, to grant this reading requires that we are able to individuate events and distinguish between alternative descriptions of the same event, and in the following, I shall assume that we can.

The decision to talk about the explanation of an event under a description of the event is, in part, a conventional one. But once it is made we need not conclude, as have many defenders of the deductive model, that all explanations are merely partial ones; and we can also avoid raising the misleading question as to whether historians explain the events with which they are concerned or only present partial explanation of them. For, as already hinted, the same event can be explained under one description and only partially explained under another more refined one. But, of course, some descriptions of events may be so general that explanations of events under them may be of little interest. However, it is not part of the deductive model to suggest which explanations are interesting; rather, to specify the conditions for the true application of "is a deductive explanation of E."

It follows that the deductive model is not concerned with an analysis of "is an explanation of T," where "T" stands in place of a name of a term or theory. Hence it is not at all strange that, in discussing the explanation of events, defenders of the deductive model proceed on the assumption that the theory that is employed for the purposes of explanation is clear in and of itself and does not require explanation. Of course, this assumption is an oversimplification and is lifted by most defenders of the deductive model when they deal with issues that arise in attempting to explain a scientific theory, or reduce it to a philosophically acceptable basis.

But though they deal first with "is an explanation of E" and then with "is an explanation of T," most defenders of the deductive model would not try to pool their results to present a unified theory of explanation of "is an explanation of D" with no restriction at all on what may be substituted for "D," providing that the result is meaningful. This is not arbitrary, but based on the conviction that there is no general problem of explanation, and that attempts to discover a general elucidation of "is an explanation of D" would lead nowhere. And though this conviction is, I think, justified, it is not, counter to the supposed arguments of some critics, essential to the model. Per contre, if the deductive model is correct and if attempts to discover a general theory of explanation succeed, then we know in advance of the construction of any such theory some of its theorems. But here critics might argue that the model has not been shown to be philosophically interesting, and the theorems presented by the model are trivial. Generally such arguments lead into bootless meta-philosophical discussions, but the argument here, or the case for these critics, may perhaps be reviewed without forays into the beyond.

Defenders of the deductive model are, above all, concerned with explanation in science. Hence the complaint of those critics that the deductive model is too formalistic and does not concern itself with the really interesting questions which play a role when scientists evaluate and decide to accept or reject a proposed explanation is, prima facie, damaging. But only prima facie, for this criticism fails to heed the point that the deductive model aims at an explication of "is an explanation of E," not of "is a warranted explanation of E" or "S knows that T explains E" or "S has rationally decided to accept T as an explanation of E." Although this criticism is not directly relevant against the model, it is, at least, in part relevant against some defenders of the deductive model who do attempt analysis of the latter phrases, and when so doing, leave themselves open to minor criticisms.

Most defenders of the deductive model assume that the degree of acceptability of a proposed explanation is an increasing function of the degree of confirmation of the statements in the explanans. But this is rather an oversimplification, or overlooks the variety of ways in which proposed explanations can be accepted. A proposed explanation may be accepted as the only explanation available, the best one of many, as one among many, as correct but shallow, as the only one available worthy of test, or as one among many worthy of development and refinement. Patently, a proposed explanation may be accepted as the only one available which is worthy of refinement, even if false or incomplete or only an explanation sketch. And no simple formula can, I think, be presented to capture the relevant considerations that enter when scientists accept explanations.

It is at best only when a proposed explanation is accepted as an explanation, as a true one, as one which can be taken as it stands, etc., that a high degree of confirmation of the statements in the explanans approaches a higher degree of its acceptability. Nevertheless, between knowing the degree of acceptability of a proposed explanation and deciding to accept it there is still a gap, and it is not part of the deductive model to give us rules in order to instruct us how and when we are to jump over it. Moreover, most defenders of the deductive model would insist that no clear rules of that sort can be given, and hence agree with those who point to the non-formal aspects of explanations; for they dissent from the claim that this is a criticism of their position.

Actually, the same answer is open to defenders of the deductive model against those who contend that there are many acceptable explanations which do not contain laws. But though this answer is available, most defenders of the deductive model cannot use it, for most of them do accept the nomological model. And though the nomological and the deductive one are logically independent, the probability of defending the deductive one and defending the nomological one is not. To defend them is not strange—they are compatible—but it is important to remember, as even some defenders of the deductive model occasionally forget, that they are not inseparable.

Thus, a defender of the nomological model might insist, as against the deductive model, that it is a mistake to seek a sufficient condition for a satisfactory explanation, insisting that we should attempt only to specify necessary ones. Moreover, he might contend that there are obvious counter-examples to the deductive model which are not counter-examples to his position; insisting, for example, that we have not explained why A's headache is gone when we note that A took aspirin, and then add that all those who take aspirin find relief from headacheness.

Of course, a defender of the nomological model, who is in sympathy with the deductive model, might not simply discard it. It is open to him to accept if it were weakened and interpreted as only stipulating necessary conditions for the deductive explanation of an event; and hence defend, as I here will, the qualified deductive model. This model stipulates a necessary condition for an explanation of an event, and another more complex one as necessary for the deductive explanation of an event. To defend such a model is, I admit, only to enter into a family squabble with the restricted deductive model; and everything that I have said in favor of the latter model applies to defend the former one as well. More-over, I am not convinced that one can justify the choice of the qualified as against the restricted one. Nevertheless, I think a few more words are necessary to illuminate the differences between these models. To do so I will use the distinction between explaining and explaining away in a non-standard manner.

The distinction between explaining away and explaining, though a hard one to make precise, is familiar enough. Frequently an experimental result is said to be explained away if at first it appears to be at variance with some theory and then is shown that such is not the case. One way of showing that the result is not at variance is to show that the result is at least to be expected, given the theory. I suggest that we generalize and discuss the explaining away of events even when the statement describing the event does not at first seem to be at variance with some theory; never-theless, all that we are able to do is to give reasons at least for expecting the event, given that the theory or lawlike statements employed are acceptable and confirmable.

Hence, information that can be used to explain an event away could have been employed to predict it, but if we allow the distinction between explaining away and explaining, we do not agree that explanation and prediction are symmetrical. Note, however, that information that can be employed to explain an event away may be used to show that the event is not idiosyncratic. Thus, we have explained away John's dislike of Bill by noting that Bill is a philosopher and add that John dislikes all philosophers. Hence we have shown that Bill's being disliked by John is not idiosyncratic, not unique to Bill, that there is nothing special about Bill, etc. But here too we have explained an event away under a description of that event.

But, of course, once we accept the nomological model, we have to agree that at least that much is done whenever we have an explanation, or agree that all explaining is at least explaining away. However, it is not part either of the nomological or qualified deductive model to offer necessary and sufficient conditions for explanation; it is not fair to demand that defenders of either of these models inform us as to what else is done whenever we explain, above and beyond explaining away. The obvious suggestion, I think, would be that, in all genuine cases of explanation, principles of certain types or laws of certain types be employed, but I do not here want to begin adumbrating the suggestion; furthermore, it would be worthless if criticisms offered by Professor Ayer and others against the applicability of the model to history and the social sciences cannot be met. Mr. Ayer has written:

> It seems to me that in history and indeed in the field of human actions generally, giving an explanation is not very often a matter of appealing to universal laws, but rather telling more of the story. We are satisfied when the story takes on a more familiar pattern, and here Dr. Popper might reply that the reason why we are satisfied is that it then comes to exemplify some universal law. But I do not think that it is true. It is sufficient for us if the account that we are given describes one of the ways we should expect such things to happen, and we do not need to believe that they always happen.[1]

Mr. Ayer's words show that the opposition to the deductive model comes not only from the idealist right and the ordinary left, but from the scientific center as well. But though the origin is different, the result is the same; for the arguments against the deductive model and its varieties, though clear, are not convincing.

Note that Mr. Ayer's argument even if granted, holds and holds only against the covering-law model. There is nothing in the deductive model that rules out the acceptance of explanations that appeal to or employ statistical laws. This appeal is also allowed for in the nomological model

---

[1] A. J. Ayer, *Proceedings of the Aristotelian Society*, supplement to vol. 22, published separately, London, Harris & Sons, 1946, pp. 175–76.

whose adherents, moreover, would insist that unless we did appeal to laws we would not have any basis for expecting certain things to happen, or for thinking that such things should happen. Hence, unless Mr. Ayer directly counters that thesis, he has no good reason to criticize the nomological model or the qualified deductive model. It may also be noted that Mr. Ayer has not given any conclusive reason for distinguishing between explanation of human actions and explanations of the behavior of non-human entities. Thus, his description of our acceptance of explanations of human behavior can be matched with descriptions of our acceptance of explanations of the behavior of cars, airplanes, toys, etc. About such entities, too, we also accept explanations that consist of stories about their make-up and past performances.

Many, I fear, would find these counter-arguments against Ayer Talmudic; for they would insist that direct observation of what we do when we accept an explanation of a human action shows that the deductive model in any of its forms does not apply. Moreover, they would not, I presume, think it essential to have to decide whether the same judgment is in order when we discuss the status of explanations of non-human entities. Of course, those who appeal to direct observation cannot be easily refuted. However, I think that direct observation may here be mistaken.

Bill goes to the refrigerator, takes out some chicken, and is asked to explain his action. He informs us that he is hungry. Here many would observe that Bill has explained his behavior and would add that it is silly to think that we know of any general laws which, when cojoined with initial conditions, make it highly probable, or give any good reason to expect, that Bill would have taken chicken from the refrigerator. But, of course, Bill has explained his action; and, of course, the nomological model, etc., does not fit. All of this we observe by simply looking the facts straight in the face.

But these critics should, I think, remember the point that we do not explain an event or action simpliciter, but explain them under a given description. Applying the dictum here, we may, I think, argue as I would argue, that Bill did not explain his action under the description of taking chicken from the refrigerator, but only under the description of taking edible food from the refrigerator. And though it might be silly to think that we know of general laws, etc., which make it highly probable that he will end up with the chicken, it is not at all silly to think that we know of general laws that make it probable that Bill, when hungry and in the house, etc., will eat something which he will first have to remove from the place where the food is kept. If my contention in this instance is correct, then inspection of the facts does not show that the qualified deductive model must either be qualified or not appealed to at all.

But here many would argue that I have not quite correctly read the facts, and that I have all too glibly assumed that when we accept explanations we do so because we know, or believe that we know, that certain lawlike statements are laws. I have previously considered and dismissed this allegation in one of its forms against the qualified deductive model, but another version of it, one which has been especially persuasive to those who are concerned with the explanation of human actions, must now be faced.

Mr. Gardiner writes:

> Hume and the empiricists generally have been wont to assume that all explanations take the form of relating one event, the explicandum, to another event or set of events which "cause" or "condition" it. This, as will be shown in detail later, is not true ...[2]

He points out that we quite frequently assert in everyday life that S did so-and-so because of a certain motive. According to Mr. Gardiner, and in this he is obviously indebted to Mr. Ryle, the ordinary interpretation would be that a motive is a certain mental occurrent that could be said to cause an act. Since Mr. Gardiner believes that there are no such mental occurrents, he thinks it absurd to maintain that they cause anything. He suggests, therefore, that motivational explanations are explanation in terms of dispositions.

The point may be illuminated, he says, by considering a convenient if crude example. Consider the statement:

> John hit you with a hammer because he is bad tempered. ... It would be absurd to deny this is an explanation, but it would be ludicrous to imagine that it could in some manner be "reduced" to an explanation asserting a causal relation between "John's bad temper" and hitting with a hammer. "John ... is bad tempered" is predictive of how John is likely to behave in various (only vaguely imagined) types of situations. ... It represents if you like an instance of how he can, in general, be expected to behave under certain conditions.[3]

[2] Patrick Gardiner, *The Nature of Historical Explanation*, London, Oxford University Press, 1952, p. 1.

[3] *Ibid.*, p. 125.

The emphasis is here drawn between causal and dispositional explanations and is discussed more fully by Mr. Gardiner in other sections of his book, but the quotations above are typical and give, I think, a fair indication of his position; a position which many find convincing, but I find dubious. Note, first, that in giving dispositional explanations we refer not only to the disposition, but to the condition under which it is manifested. John may be bad-tempered, but does not hit people with hammers under all conditions. Hence, as with causal explanations, reference must be made to occurrents.

Moreover, it is not at all apparent that we are not tacitly appealing to general laws when we give a dispositional explanation; for it would, I think, be strange to argue that John and John alone does certain types of things because he is bad-tempered and other bad-tempered people do not. Of course, John may be the only bad-tempered person alive, but that point is irrelevant. Yet there may be subtle differences between John" behavior and the behavior of other bad-tempered people, and we may then want to have a new law, which is of the form (x) (John $=$ x and x is bad-tempered ...). But such statements are still general and lawlike, as are statements about the behavior of free-falling bodies on the earth.

Finally, nothing of importance follows from the point which Mr. Gardiner emphasizes that we cannot specify general statements or statements informing us as to how John will always behave under certain types of circumstances; that is, nothing of importance follows for the topic under review. The utterances that we are prepared to make can be reconstructed as statistical ones, or as semi-statements, and we can claim that here as elsewhere we must accept explanation sketches. And if this be granted, then many who make light of the importance of explanation sketches, as construed by Professor Hempel, and take delight in dispositional explanations, are making sport of their own position.

But, as was the case with Mr. Ayer's thesis, many would find these counter-arguments perhaps interesting but overscholastic; and would insist that there is an obvious difference between causal and dispositional explanations, and that this difference has thus far not been captured and perhaps cannot be captured by those who defend the qualified deductive model. I disagree, for I do not think that a case has been made out for the claim that there are dispositional explanations; and it was only not to beg the issue that I have considered Mr. Gardiner's argument in detail. I think that in appealing to "dispositional explanations" we are not explaining why someone did something but, in the terminology suggested previously, explaining it away. If we want not merely to have good reasons for expecting John to behave this or that way, but also to know why he behaves this way, a reference to the fact that he always behaves this way will not suffice. However, a development of this thesis is not necessary in order to defend the qualified deductive model.

Neither does a follower of the qualified deductive model have to object to the thesis emphasized by Mr. Dray[4] and Mr. Gallie, among others, that historians will frequently explain an event by specifying not sufficient conditions for it, but only necessary ones. The explanation offered by Max Weber, for example, in which he insisted that Protestantism was a necessary condition for the rise of capitalism, would at best embarrass only covering-law theorists, not those who adhere to the other models we have discussed.

But even for the covering-law theorists the difficulty is only apparent. Obviously historians will not accept any statement about necessary conditions for an event as an explanation of the event. No historian will accept an explanation of the Crusades by reference to the presence of oxygen in the air, or by reference to the mere presence of Christians and Mohammedans. When they accept explanations in terms of necessary conditions, the following situation seems to obtain. A social scientist, employing the information that B is a necessary condition for A, is tacitly explaining not-A by reference to the absence of B. Thus historians will explain the decline of the Roman republic by reference to the necessary conditions for its continuation.[5] When they were not present, sufficient conditions for its decline were.

Applying this consideration to the work of Max Weber, it is clear that he did not explain the rise of capitalism in Europe by the mere reference to the presence of Protestantism. He insisted upon the importance of economic and social factors, and pointed out that a complete assessment of their relevance was required before a satisfactory explanation

[4] W. Dray, "Explanatory Narrative in History," *Philosophical Quarterly*, vol. 4 (January, 1954), 15–28.

[5] That the Roman Empire collapsed because the Roman aristocracy failed to live up to the motto of noblesse oblige is the thesis of T. Frank and M. Rostovtseff. See the former's *An Economic Survey of Ancient Rome*, Baltimore, Johns Hopkins Press, 1940, pp. 296–304; and the latter's *The Social and Economic History of the Roman Empire*, Oxford, Clarendon Press, 1926, pp. 486–87.

of the rise of capitalism would be available. He used the presence of the Protestant ethic in Europe to explain the failure of capitalistic institutions to arise in China and India. Hence his work does not present a counter-example to even the covering-law model.

Of course, in arguing that historians will at least sometimes explain an event by giving sufficient conditions for it, I am not claiming that they will be able to give sufficient conditions for every event. It is not part of the qualified deductive model to argue for determinism; neither is it part of the deductive model to assume that the distinction between the analytic and the synthetic is clear. Hence a follower of the deductive model need not disagree with those who insist that many of the generalizations employed when we explain human actions are not simply synthetic. And of course he would make the same point about the explanations offered by the physicist. Moreover he would understand why some insist that there are differences between the explanations offered by physicists and those offered by historians; he would be prepared with his counter-argument.

Physicists discuss events in the light of theories, employing their theories as guides for descriptions under which they will explain the events they consider, and hence conclude that they have explained the events with which they are concerned. Historians, not being concerned qua historians with the confirmation of general theories, do not have general guides as to what type of description to apply to events they are considering, and conclude that at best they can only give partial explanations of them. Both conclusions need not be granted if we remember that all explanations of events are explanations of them under given descriptions of them.

Of course we may want every event to be explained not only under one description but under all that are true of it. But it is part neither of history nor physics nor, as remarked, of the deductive model to accept the determinism either of the fox or the hedgehog and to claim either that for every true description of any event there is a theory that explains it under that description or that there is a theory which will explain any event and explain it under any description of it.

IX

The Role of Values in Scientific Inference

By R. B. BRAITHWAITE

I WAS doubtless asked to open a discussion upon this subject because eight years ago I devoted a disproportionately long chapter of my book *Scientific Explanation* to an exposition of Wald's minimax method for choosing between statistical hypotheses and of my reasons for preferring such a method, based upon evaluations of the consequences of believing one hypothesis when another hypothesis is true, to a method which employed an inverse probability argument from supposed prior probabilities of the hypotheses. In arguing against the inverse probability approach I am, like many middle-aged philosophers, primarily arguing with myself as a young man. The protagonists of inverse probability in the twenties—Lord Keynes, Sir Harold Jeffreys, C. D. Broad—were all living in Cambridge; and the publication of Keynes' *Treatise on Probability* was one of the great intellectual excitements of my undergraduate days. For seven or eight years I was a passionate upholder of the inverse probability approach, and I tried my hardest to patch up some of the gaps in it. My defection from it was due to F. P. Ramsey's infecting me with his skepticism. But I had nothing to put in its place until I became acquainted with Wald's work on statistical decision theory after the end of the war; and I then became as passionately devoted to considering the whole subject evaluatively or *praxeologically* (to use a term which I learned from Guilbaud) as I ever was in my youth to the inverse probability approach—though I have now become less committed to the minimax method itself. Since this paper comes toward the end of a conference during which I shall doubtless have found opportunities for criticizing inverse probability approaches, I shall devote this paper to a brief exposition of the choice-between-statistical-hypotheses part of the inductive problem, and compare (and indeed in a way conflate) the two rival justifications of methods for dealing with it. In my line of thought I owe much to D. V. Lindley's 1953 paper entitled

"Statistical Inference,"[1] which has not, I think, received the attention it deserves.

But there are two things I should say first. Sir Ronald Fisher[2] six years ago denounced the whole Neyman-Pearson-Wald approach to statistical inference in terms of decisions—choices between hypotheses—on the ground that it was only business tycoons who *decided* upon accepting a hypothesis (and he admitted that decision theory applied to statistical quality control was useful to manufacturers and Ministries of Defense). Pure scientists, according to Fisher, never definitively accept a hypothesis; they are seekers after Truth, and Truth can only be approached, never attained. Fisher's attack on decision theorists resembles K. R. Popper's criticism of an "instrumentalist" philosophy of science, which Popper says might be formulated as "the thesis that 'pure' science is a misnomer, and that all science is 'applied'."[3] On philosophical grounds I cannot subscribe to the view, common to Fisher and Popper, that there is an impassable frontier between pure science and its practical applications, between *theoria* and *praxis*: for me belief, even in the most theoretical proposition, is not independent of acting as if the belief is true. And one can perfectly well act on a belief while maintaining the "critical" attitude demanded by Popper and being prepared to abandon the belief on further evidence. Decision theory's choices between hypotheses are all *provisional* choices made on the basis of specified evidence. As the evidence increases the choice may be different, and decision theory provides methods for continuing to learn from experience. All that a praxeological decision theory presupposes is that sometimes I have to act on one or other of alternative hypotheses on the basis of the evidence I have at the time of acting. To try to find principles for acting *reasonably* in these circumstances is surely a proper task for a philosopher, and it is an uninteresting question as to whether such a philosopher should be regarded as a moral philosopher or as a philosopher of science.

The second preliminary is to answer the question why I am discussing the role of praxeological considerations in choosing a *statistical* hypothesis,

[1] *Journ. Royal Statistical Soc. B*, vol. 15, 30–65.

[2] *Journ. Royal Statistical Soc. B*, vol. 17 (1955), 69–78. Replies to his attack appeared in later issues of this journal: E. S. Pearson in vol. 17 (1955), 204–7; J. Neyman in vol. 18 (1956), 288–94.

[3] *Contemporary British Philosophy*, Series III (editor, H. D. Lewis), London, 1956, p. 377.

i.e., a hypothesis ascribing a probability (other than 1 or 0) to a member of a class β (a β-specimen) being a member of a class α (an α-specimen); and am not considering their role in the choice of a *universal* hypothesis, i.e., one stating that every (or no) β-specimen is an α-specimen. This question is easy to answer. One contrary instance is logically sufficient to refute a universal hypothesis; so evidence of one β-specimen being an α-specimen refutes every alternative universal hypothesis of the form that every β-specimen is a γ-specimen, where γ is a class exclusive to α, and no subtlety is required in choosing among the alternatives. But no statistical hypothesis is definitively refuted by the evidence of any (finite) sample of β-specimens: whatever the number of α-specimens in the sample, a hypothesis ascribing the probability p to a β-specimen being an α-specimen may still be true for every value of p except 0 and 1. Moreover the alternative hypotheses are strictly comparable, since they differ only with respect to the value of p; so the problem invites a formal treatment in which what P. Suppes has called a "model of the data"[4] is used, in which everything has been abstracted from the experiment except the number of α-specimens in the sample of β-specimens. Why it is possible to say something at this degree of abstraction is that from a statistical hypothesis H there can be deduced the conditional probability that the sample contains a specific number of α-specimens, so definite numbers are available to form the backbone of the argument.

Let us consider n simple statistical hypotheses $H_1, H_2, ..., H_n$, where H_i states that the probability of a β-specimen being an α-specimen is p_i, with $0 < p_i < 1$, for $i = 1, 2, ..., n$. Call a conditional probability on the assumption that H_i is true an H_i-probability.

A strategy of choice ("decision function") is a rule which for each of the possible numbers of α-specimens found in the sample of m β-specimens prescribes which one of the alternative hypotheses $H_1, H_2, ..., H_n$ is to be chosen. With each such strategy there is associated an $n \times n$ array, each of whose elements l_{ij} (i, j = 1, 2, ..., n) is the H_j-probability of H_i being chosen by the strategy. These H_j-probabilities are functions only of p_j, since they are sums of terms in the binomial expansion $(p_j + q_j)^m$, where $q_j = 1 - p_j$. The elements in the jth column of the array, which are all H_j-probabilities, depend only upon p_j. And the elements in each column add up to 1, since by the conditions of the problem one and only

---

[4] *Synthèse*, vol. 12 (1960), 297.

one hypothesis must be chosen. The diagonal elements in the array are all probabilities of the strategy yielding a correct choice, i.e., of choosing H_i if H_i is true; the non-diagonal elements are the probabilities of incorrect choice, i.e., of choosing H_i if H_j is true, for $j \neq i$. It is unnecessary to consider both correct and incorrect choices, since the strategy prescribes a choice in every case, and so the sum of the probabilities in each column is 1. When $n > 2$ there are more incorrect than correct choices; so it is convenient to omit the diagonal elements in the array which correspond to correct choices. They can be replaced whenever required by inserting a number which brings the column-sum up to 1. Such $n \times n$ arrays, with no diagonal elements, will be called *Lindley arrays*.

The simplest case in which all the logical problems arise is that in which $n = 3$, so that there are three alternative hypotheses to choose between, and $m = 1$, so that the evidence available in making the choice is whether the one β-specimen in the sample is or is not an α-specimen. In this case there are nine possible strategies of choice, which will be designated by T_{rs} ($r, s = 1, 2, 3$), T_{rs} being the strategy which chooses H_r or H_s accordingly as the unique β-specimen of the sample is or is not an α-specimen. The nine Lindley arrays corresponding to these nine strategies have (non-diagonal) elements l_{ij} ($i \neq j$) given in the columns headed $l_{21}, l_{31}, l_{12}, l_{32}, l_{13}, l_{23}$ in the table following on page 184.

The three columns headed $l_{21} + l_{31}$, $l_{12} + l_{32}$, $l_{13} + l_{23}$ give the probabilities, on H_1, H_2, H_3 respectively, of the strategy in question yielding one or other incorrect choice, since if H_1 is true, a choice of either H_2 (with H_1-probability l_{21}) or of H_3 (with H_1-probability l_{31}) will be incorrect. These will be called the *improbabilities* (on H_1, H_2, H_3 respectively) *of correct choice*. The probability of correct choice is, of course, in each case $1 -$ (the improbability of correct choice).

The problem of choice between statistical hypotheses is that of finding a suitable policy for selecting a "best" strategy.

Let us first see what plausible policies can be suggested when nothing whatever is to be taken into account except the probabilities given in the table. Since the entries in the table are all probabilities (or sums of probabilities) of incorrect choice, the problem is that of selecting a suitable *minimizing* policy; the difficulty is that there are several different functions of these probabilities which it is plausible to wish to minimize. I shall explain and discuss two plausible minimizing methods. In what follows I shall suppose that $p_1 > p_2 > p_3$.

Strategy	Elements of Lindley array						Improbabilities of correct choice			Sum
	l_{21}	l_{31}	l_{12}	l_{32}	l_{13}	l_{23}	$l_{21} + l_{31}$	$l_{12} + l_{32}$	$l_{13} + l_{23}$	
T_{11}	0	0	1	0	1	0	0	1	1	2
T_{12}	q_1	0	p_2	0	p_3	q_3	q_1	p_2	1	$2 - (p_1 - p_2)$
T_{13}	0	q_1	p_2	q_2	p_3	0	q_1	1	p_3	$2 - (p_1 - p_3)$
T_{23}	p_1	q_1	0	q_2	0	p_3	1	q_2	p_3	$2 - (p_2 - p_3)$
T_{22}	1	0	0	0	0	1	1	0	1	2
T_{32}	q_1	p_1	0	p_2	0	q_3	1	p_2	q_3	$2 + (p_2 - p_3)$
T_{31}	0	p_1	q_2	p_2	q_3	0	p_1	1	q_3	$2 + (p_1 - p_3)$
T_{21}	p_1	0	q_2	0	q_3	p_3	p_1	q_2	1	$2 + (p_1 - p_2)$
T_{33}	0	1	0	1	0	0	1	1	0	2

THE LEAST-SUM POLICY

Select that strategy (the *least-sum strategy*) which minimizes the sum of the improbabilities of correct choice (these sums are given in the last column of the table). For our case in which $p_1 > p_2 > p_3$, this policy selects the strategy T_{13}, i.e. that of choosing H_1 or H_3 accordingly as the sample contains one or no a-specimen. It is easy to show that this policy is identical with Fisher's *maximum likelihood method*: the H_1-likelihood of the sample containing one a-specimen, which is p_1, is greater than the H_2- or H_3-likelihoods, which are p_2 and p_3 respectively; and the H_3-likelihood of the sample containing no a-specimen, which is q_3 ($= 1 - p_3$), is greater than the H_1- or H_2-likelihoods, q_1 and q_2 respectively.

THE LEAST-EQUALIZING POLICY

First select the class of strategies for each of which the H_1-, H_2- and H_3-improbabilities of correct choice are the same, and then select out of this class of *equalizing* strategies the *least-equalizing strategy* which yields the minimum of these improbabilities.

This policy is inapplicable if we limit ourselves to the use of only one or other of the nine strategies, since (except in very special cases) none of them are equalizing. But if we allow ourselves the use of randomized or *mixed* strategies (i.e., probability mixtures of some or all of the nine *pure* strategies), there will always be equalizing strategies, indeed an infinite number of them; and we can choose from this class the least equalizing strategy yielding the least improbability of correct choice.

For our case in which $p_1 > p_2 > p_3$ it can be shown that the pure strategies T_{32}, T_{31}, T_{21} will never appear in the probability mixture making up the least-equalizing strategy T_0; which of the other strategies will appear depends upon complicated relations between the values of p_1, p_2, p_3. But it is easy to calculate T_0 in any particular case. For a typical case in which $p_1 = 0.6$, $p_2 = 0.3$, $p_3 = 0.2$, T_0 is the mixed strategy which can be obtained *either* by mixing T_{12}, T_{13}, T_{23} with probabilities $27/57$, $13/57$, $17/57$ respectively *or* by mixing T_{12}, T_{13}, T_{22} with probabilities $10/57$, $30/57$, $17/57$ respectively (or, of course, by mixing these two mixtures in any probability mixture).

These two policies—the least-sum policy and the least-equalizing policy—have a simple geometrical representation in two- or three-dimensional Euclidean space when the problem is that of choice between two or among three hypotheses. For our case with three hypotheses, represent the nine possible pure strategies of choice by nine points specified, in each case, by taking the H_1-improbability of correct choice as the x co-ordinate, the H_2-improbability as the y co-ordinate and the H_3-improbability as the z co-ordinate. These nine *strategy points* are the vertices of a nonahedron (of whose faces five are parallelograms and four are triangles), and every point on or inside the nonahedron represents a mixed strategy. (The strategy points are all the points of the *convex covering* of the nine pure strategy points.) The strategy point representing the *least-sum strategy* is the point where the nonahedron is touched from below by a plane whose Cartesian equation is $x + y + z = $ constant. The strategy point representing the *least-equalizing strategy* is the lowest point common to both the nonahedron and the line $x = y = z$.

From this geometrical representation it is easy to see (1) that the least-sum policy will provide a unique strategy, which is a pure strategy, unless one of the lower edges or faces of the nonahedron lies in a plane whose equation is $x + y + z =$ constant, in which case all the points in this edge or face represent least-sums; (2) that the least-equalizing policy will always provide a unique strategy, which will be a mixed strategy unless one of the lower vertices of the nonahedron lies on the line $x = y = z$.

The case we have considered is that in which the number m in the sample is only 1. As m increases, the polyhedron of the strategy points expands to fill more and more of the unit cube, and the strategy points provided by the two policies both get nearer and nearer to the point $(0, 0, 0)$, i.e., the improbability of correct choice according to either of the policies tends to zero. A policy for selecting a "best" strategy for which this is not the case would not be plausible; and it is this asymptotic property of both the least-sum and the least-equalizing policies that gives them their claims to consideration.

So far nothing has been said to justify use of either of the policies. The Fisher school of statisticians believe that no justification is required for the least-sum policy (equivalent to Fisher's maximum-likelihood method) apart from the excellence of its asymptotic properties. But all plausible policies have very similar asymptotic properties; and we are interested in knowing which policy to prefer when the sample is not very large. Also a philosopher must be concerned with justification and cannot be satisfied in using a method without good reason.

The least-equalizing policy can be justified by praxeological considerations. Suppose that the six losses which would be suffered by choosing H_i if H_j is true, for $i, j = 1, 2, 3, i \neq j$, are the same. Then the numbers giving the H_1-, H_2-, H_3-improbabilities of correct choice for any strategy of choice will also serve to measure the mathematical expectations of the loss which will be suffered if the strategy is used and if H_1, H_2, H_3 respectively are true. The least-equalizing policy will then provide a strategy which will yield the same expectation of loss (call this *prospective loss*) whichever hypothesis is true. To use the least-equalizing strategy is to remove *uncertainty* (as opposed to chance); the prospective loss is independent of which hypothesis in fact is true. This prospective loss will be less than the loss which might be suffered under one or other of the hypotheses if any other strategy were used; so the least-equalizing strategy is a *minimax* strategy: the maximum over the three hypotheses of the losses which would be suffered by using the least-equalizing strategy is a minimum over the strategies of these maxima. So to use a least-equalizing strategy is to attain the highest possible *security level* (to use R. D. Luce and H. Raiffa's expression);[5] such a policy has therefore been called one of *prudence*, or of *caution*, and even one of *pessimism*, since it secures the best that can be obtained if Nature were supposed to be working directly against the hypothesis-chooser. A minimax strategy, as has been said, makes the best of the worst of all possible worlds.

I have deliberately specified the least-equalizing strategy in terms of the equality of its yields on any of the hypotheses in question instead of in terms of its property of minimaximizing prospective loss (or improbability of correct choice), because it is the former property that I wish to emphasize. In the general theory of two-person, wholly competitive (zero-sum) games the minimax property is all-important, since it is only in some games that the minimax strategy is an equalizing strategy for either or both of the players. But in the "games against Nature" which correspond to our problem of choice between simple statistical hypotheses, a minimax strategy for the hypothesis-chooser will always be one which equalizes his yield on each hypothesis; so the least-equalizing property can be taken as specifying the strategy. (A minimax strategy for Nature in this game would not be equalizing.) Geometrically the equivalence of the least-equalizing property and the minimax property arises from the fact that the polyhedron of strategy points will, in the case (for example) of choice between three simple hypotheses, always have $(0, 1, 1)$, $(1, 0, 1)$, $(1, 1, 0)$ as vertices, so that a ray rising from the origin will always intersect the polyhedron.

The justification which most logicians have given for the least-sum method is an inverse-probability argument. Suppose that the prior probabilities of the three hypotheses are equal. Then the ratios of the posterior probabilities will, by Bayes' Theorem, be the same as the ratios of the likelihoods; so the least-sum policy, which chooses the hypothesis yielding the maximum likelihood, will choose the hypothesis whose posterior probability is greatest.

Such a justification is of no avail to a logician who wishes to make no use of inverse probability arguments, either because he can give no meaning to the notion of the probability of a hypothesis, whether prior or posterior, or because he can see no reason for assigning a number to measure a prior probability. But it is possible to base a justification of the least-sum method on praxeological considerations. If we suppose, as

---

[5] *Games and Decisions* (New York, John Wiley & Sons, 1957), p. 66.

before, that the six losses which would be suffered by choosing H_i if H_j is true are equal, for i, j = 1, 2, 3, i ≠ j, the least-sum policy will prescribe a choice of that strategy which minimizes the *aggregate* of the prospective losses for each of the three hypotheses, or (which comes to the same thing) which minimizes the *average* prospective loss, averaged over the three hypotheses.

But, it will be asked, what plausible reason can be given for considering the sum (or the average) of the prospective losses, when only one of the losses can in fact occur? An optimist might reply that he preferred the least-sum policy to the least-equalizing policy in that the former gave Nature the opportunity of giving him more than the security level, which is the most that the latter would allow Nature to give. If it be then retorted that it would be still better for the optimist to choose that strategy whose row, in the table of improbabilities of correct choice, contained the minimum of all the entries, so that if the hypothesis which would yield this minimum were to be true he would be better off than by choosing any other strategy, the optimist could reply that he was not as optimistic as all that; it would be rash to assume that Nature would co-operate with him to that extent, but less rash to assume that Nature would not positively try to do him down. A proper balance of optimism and prudence, he might say, requires that he should do all that he could to minimize his loss, on the assumption that Nature's choice of the true hypothesis will be independent of his choice of strategy; and this he would do by choosing a strategy which minimized the average loss.

Of course if he expands the assumption that Nature's choice of the true hypothesis is independent of his choice of strategy into the assumption that the prior probabilities of the hypotheses are equal, he is back to using the inverse-probability justification. Historically, an assumption of equal prior probabilities has frequently been defended, or excused, by a principle of "indifference" permitting the ascription of equal prior probabilities to propositions in circumstances in which there was no reason to believe one rather than another. But that Nature's choice is independent of that of the hypothesis-chooser is a weaker assumption than that of assuming equal prior probabilities for the hypotheses, and, indeed, can be made by a person unwilling to use the notion of prior probability at all.

There is a sort of analogy, which I mention for what it is worth, between the question of deciding, on praxeological considerations, between the least-sum policy and the least-equalizing policy and the econo-mico-political question of deciding between a policy of producing greatest aggregate happiness and the policy of equalizing the happinesses of individuals at as high a level as possible. Bentham's utilitarianism, which aimed at maximizing aggregate happiness without regard to how it was distributed, cannot escape the objection that there is no person who can have an aggregated happiness, and no average man who can have the average of the happinesses of all men. Whether or not this impossibility is of the same kind as the logical impossibility of two simple statistical hypotheses both being true is a philosophical question which need not concern us. But, supposing that the happinesses of individuals can be measured interpersonally so that meaning can be given to the sum of two person's happinesses, the policy of maximizing this sum can be defended on the ground that it increases the average happiness without having to suppose that there is anyone who can have this average happiness. The egalitarian will, of course, defend his policy by pointing out its minimax and equalizing properties; that it will maximize the minimum which each person will receive and ensure that each person receives the same.

My aim in this discussion has been to show that the least-sum policy for choosing between statistical hypotheses can, like the least-equalizing policy, have a justification on praxeological lines, so that a person who prefers the former to the latter need not feel compelled to justify it by inverse probability arguments.

Let us now pass from the simplest case in which nothing is allowed to enter into our calculations except the probabilities given in the table to the case in which we are prepared to weight these probabilities by multiplying them by weighting factors. Let us suppose first that we multiply by positive numbers u_1, u_2, u_3 all the entries in the columns which refer to probabilities (or improbabilities) given the truth of H_1, H_2, H_3, respectively (i.e., for the improbabilities of correct choice $l_{21} + l_{31}$ will be multiplied by u_1; $l_{12} + l_{32}$ by u_2; $l_{13} + l_{23}$ by u_3). If we apply the least-sum policy to the weighted entries and wish to justify this by an inverse probability argument, we shall interpret the ratios of u_1, u_2, u_3 as the ratios of the prior probabilities of H_1, H_2, H_3, respectively, and use Bayes' Theorem to show that the ratios of the posterior probabilities are the ratios of the prior probabilities multiplied by the ratios of the corre-sponding likelihoods. If we apply either the least-sum policy or the least equalizing policy to the weighted entries and justify these by praxeological considerations, we shall interpret u_1, u_2, u_3 as the losses we shall incur by incorrect choice when H_1, H_2, H_3, respectively, are true (i.e., if b_{ij} is the loss which would be suffered by choosing H_i if H_j is true, for i, j = 1, 2, 3, i $\neq$ j, we take $b_{21} = b_{31} = u_1$, $b_{12} = b_{32} = u_2$, $b_{13} = b_{23} = u_3$). The weighted entries which either policy will employ in its calculation will thus be the prospective losses $u_1(l_{21} + l_{31})$, etc., to be expected if the strategy is used.

Geometrically the weighting of the probabilities by positive weighting factors u_1, u_2, u_3 may be regarded as expanding or contracting the nonahedron of the strategy points in the directions of the three axes by factors u_1, u_2, u_3, respectively. The point where a supporting plane touches from below the distorted nonahedron, or where a ray from the origin hits the distorted nonahedron, is clearly not affected by the way in which the distortion is regarded—whether as one allowing for differing prior probabilities or as one allowing for differing losses by incorrect choice. And if the number of the sample is increased so that the distorted polyhedron of strategy points fills more and more of the unit cube, the role of the distortion diminishes in importance in settling a "best" strategy, in whichever way the distortion is regarded.

A believer in the notion of prior probability may nevertheless not wish to justify his policy of choice purely by considerations of inverse probability, but may also wish to introduce praxeological considerations. In that case he will introduce two triads of weighting factors (all positive) —one triad u_1, u_2, u_3 with ratios representing the ratios of prior probabilities of the three hypotheses; and the other triad v_1, v_2, v_3 representing the losses incurred by incorrect choice in these three cases. The weighted entries in the table used for calculation will then be the entries in the original table multiplied by u_1v_1, by u_2v_2, by u_3v_3, accordingly as the original entries refer to probabilities (or improbabilities) given the truth of H_1, H_2, H_3, respectively. The least-sum strategy derived from this new table will be a strategy which minimizes the (u_1, u_2, u_3)-weighted average prospective loss, averaged over the three hypotheses. Since the weighting factors u_1, u_2, u_3 are being regarded as proportional to prior probabilities, this weighted average prospective loss will be the mathematical expectation of prospective loss, i.e., the *strategy prospective loss* to be expected by using the least-sum strategy. If in the second triad of weighting factors $v_1 = v_2 = v_3$, the least-sum strategy will be the same as that arrived at by a Bayes' Theorem argument, now justified as minimizing prospective loss.

An important feature of this situation (to which Lindley was the first to call attention) is that, so far as the calculation of either the least-sum strategy or the least-equalizing strategy is concerned, the separate values in the pairs u_1, v_1; u_2, v_2; u_3, v_3 are irrelevant. All that are relevant are the products u_1v_1, u_2v_2, u_3v_3. Call these products w_1, w_2, w_3, respectively. A disbeliever in prior probability will (if he uses the least-sum strategy) select axactly the same strategy as the ascriber of prior probabilities in the ratio $u_1 : u_2 : u_3$ if he takes for the losses incurred by incorrect choice on the three hypotheses w_1, w_2, w_3 instead of the v_1, v_2, v_3 of the ascriber. And, vice versa, an ascriber of prior probabilities who wishes to limit the praxeological consideration he introduces to that of an equally bad mark if his choice of hypothesis is incorrect will select exactly the same strategy as he would have done had he gone further down the praxeological path and taken the losses incurred by incorrect choices to be v_1, v_2, v_3, provided that in the former case he ascribes prior probabilities in the ratio $w_1 : w_2 : w_3$ instead of in the ratio $u_1 : u_2 : u_3$ of the latter case

The situation is not very different if we take the general case of Wald's original praxeological discussion of the problem, where we do not suppose that the loss to be incurred if H_j is true and H_i is chosen is the same for every $i \neq j$. We shall then be concerned with six distinct losses: b_{21}, b_{31}, b_{12}, b_{32}, b_{13}, b_{23}. If we are not also introducing weighting factors corresponding to prior probabilities, the entries in the original table will be modified by taking $b_{ij}l_{ij}$ instead of l_{ij} for $i, j = 1, 2, 3$, $i \neq j$, in the Lindley arrays, and hence $b_{21}l_{21} + b_{31}l_{31}$, $b_{12}l_{12} + b_{32}l_{32}$, $b_{13}l_{13} + b_{23}l_{23}$ as the prospective losses to be expected by using the strategy in question if H_1, H_2, H_3, respectively, are true. If we also introduce weighting factors u_1, u_2, u_3, whose ratio is that of the supposed prior probabilities, the prospective losses to be expected by using the strategy in question will be $u_1(b_{21}l_{21} + b_{31}l_{31})$, $u_2(b_{12}l_{12} + b_{32}l_{32})$, $u_3(b_{13}l_{13} + b_{23}l_{23})$. (Least-sum strategies calculated by means of these strategy prospective losses are called *Bayes strategies*—or Bayes solutions of the decision problem—in the literature of statistical decision theory.) The least-sum strategy selected by a disbeliever in prior probability will therefore be exactly the same as the Bayes strategy of the ascriber of prior probabilities in the ratio $u_1 : u_2 : u_3$; if the six distinct losses of the former a_{ij} are related to those of the latter b_{ij} by the equalities $a_{ij} = u_jb_{ij}$, for $i, j = 1, 2, 3$, $i \neq j$.

Thus in the general case the six weighting factors a_{ij} which, together with the probabilities of incorrect choice, determine both the least-sum and the least-equalizing strategies, may be given two interpretations—either as representing the losses to be suffered by choosing H_i if H_j is true, or as representing the ratios of the prospective losses to be suffered by choosing H_i if H_j has a given prior probability. A disbeliever in prior probability can obtain exactly the same weighted table to employ in his calculation of a "best" strategy as an ascriber of prior probabilities by taking the latter's six prospective losses as being six losses.

My conclusion is that, by permitting praxeological considerations, we can have almost all the advantages which ascribers of prior probabilities claim for their procedure without the grave disadvantage of using a philosophically dubious notion. The one exception is that, if we wish to use the least-sum policy rather than the least-equalizing policy, we cannot justify the former as giving the least strategy-prospective loss, but must justify it either in the hopeful way that I have indicated or by arguments similar to those of H. Chernoff[6] and J. Milnor[7], which raise questions of a different nature which I have not been able to discuss in this paper.

As a coda to this piece, I shall mention a proposal for a compromise with the prior-probability ascribers put forward by Lindley. He suggests that the ascriber's product of weighting factors, $u_j b_{ij}$, should be regarded as a single weighting factor a_{ij}, but that this should not be interpreted as simply a loss but as representing the "seriousness" of the choice of H_i when H_j is true. "Loss," Lindley says, "is not easily separated in our own minds from beliefs. Conversely I feel that prior beliefs are only beliefs for action, that is, contain an element of loss in them ... If this is correct, I see no reason why we should try to separate the ideas, since in applications this is not necessary" (loc. cit. p. 46).

This proposal to take as data neither losses nor prior probabilities, but what I shall call *seriosities*, presents, I think, no great difficulty with regard to their internal logic. Since it is a fundamental characteristic of mathematical expectations that expectations of expectations are themselves expectations, seriosities (assuming that they can be simply ordered) can be measured on an interval scale of "degrees of seriosity" just as utilities can be measured on an interval scale by the probability-combination-indifference method of Ramsey and von Neumann & Morgenstern.

[6] *Econometrica*, vol. 22 (1954), 422–43.

[7] R. M. Thrall et al., *Decision Processes*, New York, John Wiley & Sons, 1954, 49–59.

Complications will arise if a sub-class of seriosities is known to contain no element of uncertainty, i.e., are losses; but if such a sub-class can be distinguished, it might serve as a basis for measuring the uncertainty contained in the others. The great difficulty would be the relation of the seriosities to objective fact. I bet upon the fall of dice taking account of expectations of utilities, and when the dice have fallen know how many degrees of utility I have gained or lost. But if I bet upon the fall of dice about whose lack of bias I am uncertain and therefore take account of expectations of seriosities, it is still degrees of utility and not degrees of seriosity that I shall gain or lose. So there could be no backward-looking judgment as to the propriety of my seriosity evaluations. Nevertheless, I offer a present of seriosities to those who wish to incorporate prior uncertainty into their inductive methods, since seriosities might possibly be worked into a form more acceptable to empirically-minded philosophers than has proved to be the case with prior probabilities.

Opening Statement

By Braithwaite

T HERE is a point not mentioned in my paper which perhaps is worth remarking upon, since it has not been discussed in the literature of statistical decision theory. The rectangular array in which each row represents one of the alternative strategies and each column the improbabilities of correct choice (or, alternatively, the prospective losses), given the truth of one of the alternative hypotheses, is normally used as a basis for choosing a strategy on the strength of some beliefs about the prior probabilities of the alternative hypotheses (except for a choice made in accordance with the least-equalizing policy, where no such beliefs are required). If one of the hypotheses is believed to be certain (i.e., to have a prior probability of 1), all the columns except its column are irrelevant; and the strategy to be chosen is that which contains the minimum of the entries in that column. But the rectangular array can be looked at the other way around, and used as a basis for choosing a column rather than a row. I could first decide upon the strategy, pure or mixed, which I proposed to employ, and on the strength of this decision use the least-sum policy to select the hypothesis which it is "best" for me to believe. (I could also use the minimax policy, which would only in very special cases be least-equalizing, to select the distribution of prior probabilities over the hypotheses, assignment of which would give me the highest "security level.") Consideration of the inverted array will thus provide a rationale for "wishful thinking," for my selecting my beliefs so as to fit in best with what I have already decided to do, or indeed done. To choose one's beliefs in this way may well be held to be conduct which is irrational as well as immoral; but it is interesting to see that there is a logic of wishful thinking which closely parallels the logic of statistical decision theory.

To return to the matters discussed in my paper. For the case of choice between two simple statistical hypotheses, where my geometrical representation of the possible strategies is a polygon in the (x, y) plane with (0, 1) as the highest and most leftward vertex and (1, 0) as the lowest and most rightward, the choice of strategy given by the Bayes Theorem argument used by an ascriber of equal prior probabilities will be determined by the point (or points on the side) of the polygon where it is touched from below by a straight line whose slope is -1. If this polygon is expanded or contracted in the directions of the axes by positive weighting factors, the point of tangency of the line of slope -1 may well be different, in which case a different strategy will be chosen. One of the principal points made in my paper was that the same strategy would be chosen (in accordance with the least-sum policy) in whatever way the weighting factors are interpreted—whether as prior probabilities or as losses or as products of one of these with the other ("seriosities"). A praxeological approach using the least-sum policy will, therefore, with a suitable weighting of the losses, yield exactly the same strategy as a non-praxeological prior-probability approach; though if the praxeological approach does not include any assigning of prior probabilities, it will not be possible to defend the least-sum policy by a Bayes Theorem argument.

With regard to the least-equalizing policy, which can be defended praxeologically (as removing uncertainty and securing the highest possible "security level") without any reference to prior probabilities, there is one point about its relation to the least-sum policy which I did not make, explicitly, in my paper. In my two-dimensional, geometrical representation for the choice between two hypotheses, the least-equalizing strategy is represented by the point where a ray of slope 1 rising from the origin hits the polygon. If the polygon is expanded or contracted vertically or horizontally by positive weighting factors, the least-equalizing strategy point will vary, and it will be possible to select weighting factors in such a way that any point on the lower boundary of the polygon (excluding the two end points) will be the least-equalizing strategy point. So any strategy point given by employing the least-equalizing policy will also be given by employing the least-sum policy with a suitable adjustment in the weighting, and vice versa (except for the end points). Since this correspondence arises solely out of the mathematics of the situation, it depends in no way upon how either of the weightings is interpreted—whether as prior probabilities, losses, or seriosities.

Where more than two hypotheses are concerned, there will be more possibilities of interpreting the weighting factors if praxeological considerations are introduced than if they have to be interpreted purely as prior probabilities. This opening of more possibilities is, I suspect, one reason why so many contemporary mathematical statisticians use praxeological considerations in their systematic approach, although most of them have no qualms about ascribing prior probabilities to the hypotheses to yield "Bayes strategies" whenever they find this convenient.

Comments on Braithwaite Paper

By Henry E. Kyburg, Jr.

T HERE are four things that bother me about Professor Braithwaite's paper.

The most serious difficulty I have with Braithwaite's paper is one which arises out of my complete agreement with Fisher's contention that it is only business tycoons who make decisions of the sort dealt with by decision theory. The difficulty with the praxeological approach is not that, since actions either take place or do not, we are committed to definitively accepting or definitively rejecting hypotheses, while in fact hypotheses cannot be definitively confirmed or refuted. What is objectionable—and I should say even morally objectionable—in decision theory is that the complex interdependence of action and belief is covered up with such ambiguous generalities as "For me, belief, even in the most theoretical proposition, is not independent of acting as if the belief is true."

Of course action and belief are not independent. But I may act on hypotheses that I am nearly certain are false: e.g., if someone tells me that a mysterious stranger just slipped something that looked like a hundred-dollar bill into my coat pocket, I shall reject the hypothesis as absurd; but I'll look in my coat pocket just the same. That is, I shall *act* on the exceedingly unlikely hypothesis that the stranger did slip a hundred-dollar bill into my pocket.

Fundamentally, I should maintain that actions and beliefs are simply quite different sorts of things. Nouns denoting actions and nouns denoting beliefs are followed by quite different sorts of verbs: actions *occur*, beliefs are *held*, and so on. It is true (but not very startling) that actions are the best—and so far as other people's beliefs are concerned, the only—way we have of finding out about beliefs. But to say that this means that they are the same thing seems to me a naïve form of behaviorism. The form of behaviorism embraced by decision theory is even worse than naïve, since not only are all beliefs reduced to collections of actions (or potential actions), but they are to be reduced to actions of a very simple standard sort; namely, the exchange of utilities which, like dollars, are supposed to be comparable to every sort of value. The utilities we deal with in decision theory can be cashed in for anything we want.

Braithwaite argues for a praxeological approach only in a preliminary paragraph; I have commented at length only because I think it is a very serious question indeed whether to commit oneself entirely to this approach, as Braithwaite seems to wish to do. In certain situations the praxeological approach is perfectly natural and sensible; in manufacturing we are often concerned with choices between actions (and devil take hypotheses), where the consequences of each action can be neatly quantified by ordinary accounting procedures. And it is a perfectly legitimate, though perhaps rather limited, function of a philosopher to "try to find principles for acting *reasonably* in these circumstances." (see p. 181).

My next two comments concern matters of detail. First, Braithwaite's least-sum policy is, to judge by the behavioristic criteria that he applies to beliefs, just a Bayesian approach with the assignment of equal a priori probabilities to the alternative hypotheses. Braithwaite attempts to justify the least-sum policy by speaking of minimizing the average loss. But of course the word "average" can be used in the sense of "expectation" or "mean" only if we have a priori probabilities for the alternative hypotheses; and it is difficult to see what sense we can make of it without prior probabilities. It is true that we are directed to take the average of several numbers; but I can see no justification for using this average as a guide to action unless it is an expectation; nor do I think it makes good sense to call it an "average loss," unless it is the first moment of a random variable.

I have a similar difficulty understanding the notion, used later on to justify the consideration of the average loss, that "Nature's choice of the true hypothesis [!] is independent of his [the scientist's] choice of strategy." (p. 188). Again, while it makes good sense to talk of stochastic independence holding between hypothesis and strategy, if we are willing to talk about a priori probability distributions, I find it difficult to imagine what kind of "independence" is involved that is not of that sort. And, referring to the same paragraph, if we do suppose that independence is stochastic independence, we require, in order to minimize our losses, not only that Nature's choice of the true hypothesis be stochastically independent of our choice of strategy, but also that the probability of choice of a given hypothesis be the same as the probability of choice of any other hypothesis. Independence is weaker than equal a priori probabilities, as Braithwaite says; but it fails to do what Braithwaite would like it to do. Perhaps, on the other hand, my difficulty stems from a failure to penetrate the deep metaphor of Nature choosing a hypothesis.

My second minor point concerns seriosities. In the later portion of his paper, Braithwaite introduces weighting factors, which may be interpreted as a priori probabilities, as utilities, or as products of a priori probabilities and utilities. The point which Braithwaite brings out—and it is a very important one indeed—is that so far as the praxeological approach is concerned it makes no difference how we interpret these numbers. However we interpret them, we still have in the final analysis a set of numbers with which we will deal either by a least-sum policy or a least-equalizing policy. But Braithwaite could carry his analysis one step farther than he does. He says, "The least-sum strategy selected by a disbeliever in prior probability will therefore be exactly the same as the Bayes strategy of the ascriber of prior probabilities in the ratio $u_1 : u_2 : u_3$, if the six distinct losses of the former a_{ij} are related to those of the latter b_{ij} by the equalities $a_{ij} = u_j b_{ij}$." (p. 191). The additional step is this: if we are given the six numbers a_{ij}, and if we suppose that there is any admixture of prior probabilities in these numbers—that is, if we suppose that they are not pure utilities, but are utilities weighted by likelihoods—then we must *always* use a least-sum strategy (i.e., a Bayes' strategy) rather than a least equalizing strategy, simply because the expected loss under the former is less than the expected loss under the latter strategy. (And here we are using "expected loss" in the standard technical sense.)

Observe that we don't have to have an analysis of the numbers a_{ij} into their utility and prior-probability components; all we have to suppose is that some such analysis is proper. Thus we must either reject the notion of prior probability completely, or else we are permanently committed to least-sum strategies.

I come now to my final point. Braithwaite says, "Also a philosopher must be concerned with justification and cannot be satisfied in using a method without good reason." (p. 186). His objection, and in fact the classical objection, to the Bayes method is the following well-known difficulty: If we have a choice between n hypotheses, none of which is extreme (i.e., conclusively refutable), then whatever the evidence may be, and whatever finite values may be assigned to the various errors, there exists for every i, $1 \leqslant i \leqslant n$, an assignment of a priori probabilities to the hypotheses such that we will be directed to choose the i'th hypothesis on the basis of the given evidence. Furthermore, there is no *good reason* for picking one set of a priori probabilities rather than another one. And so there seems to be no philosophically satisfying reason not to pick the hypothesis H_1 first, and then to assign a priori probabilities in such a way that our Bayes strategy directs us to accept H_1. The same thing will be true of the numbers a_{ij} whether we regard them as prior probabilities, utilities, or the combination which Braithwaite suggests calling "seriosities". And in fact the same thing will be true whether we use a least-sum policy or a least-equalizing policy. Given any evidence, there will be, for every hypothesis H_i, an assignment of numbers a_{ij} such that we will be directed to choose (act on) hypothesis H_i. I know of no way of specifying seriosities which is any better than the subjective way of specifying prior probabilities; in either case the set of numbers is arbitrary. But this is simply to say that any form of behavior is reasonable—given the set of arbitrary numbers that will rationalize it. We have not succeeded in finding "principles for acting reasonably." Braithwaite's seriosity gambit, rather than saving the respectability of the Bayes solution to the decision problem, has only succeeded in making the praxeological justification of the minimax policy as dubious as the subjectivist justification of the Bayes strategy.

Discussion on Braithwaite Paper

(Based on notes by HENRY FINCH)

BLACK: It seems to me that the central point at issue is what I will call the paradox of the arbitrary choice of hypotheses. On the theory that Braithwaite is expounding, we can make an arbitrary choice of one of a given set of hypotheses and then adjust, *post hoc*, the utilities, a priori probabilities, or whatever, to end up having to choose a given one of the hypotheses. This sounds to me like a *reductio ad absurdum* of the whole program. A second point concerns the distinction between belief and action. The whole notion of acting on a proposition requires clarification. A third point is whether, in this model, we have a right to talk about Nature choosing. It's one thing to imagine the scientist behaving as a decision-maker, but it seems to me that in attributing this role to Nature as well, we are in danger of falling prey to the idol of the casino; it is difficult to imagine Nature as a croupier playing against the scientist. Finally, we may ask, what action is relevant to the choice of a universal, general, statistical hypothesis? It is not clear what difference in action it makes whether one chooses H_1 or H_2. It is not just a question of choosing a black rather than a white on the next draw, because this choice does not reflect the actual numbers involved. All of this suggests that statistical inference is begotten by decision upon ignorance.

BRAITHWAITE: "Nature choosing" is a metaphor which can be helpful from the point of view of the theory of games. All I meant by the independence of Nature's choice of hypotheses was that whether they are true or false does not depend on us.

BLACK: An heir-problem to the classical problem of induction seems to have emerged, if you are right. No longer is it a question whether to believe or not; rather we are to see what can be done, and we must become moral critics.

BRAITHWAITE: I am not averse to that.

*   *   *

MORGENBESSER: What bearing has your policy upon the question of accepting universally quantified laws and broad complexes of "overarching" theory? How can an action in these domains be connected with utilities? It is difficult to see how in these cases the alternative hypotheses that we are choosing between can be framed. One might define seriosities in terms of the seriousness of the changes in the conceptual framework entailed by the truth of one or another of subsidiary hypotheses.

BRAITHWAITE: I admit that I was discussing a limited problem, namely, the acceptance or rejection of statistical hypotheses.

*   *   *

BERLYNE: To bridge the gap between "truth" and "utility," motivation should be brought in; we must consider such losses as surprise, shock, doubts, uncertainties, and possibly information content, the relevance of the latter having been recently recognized by Hempel. He suggested that hypothesis-choosing might be discussed in these terms; it might be a matter of choosing the hypothesis that gives you the most information, in Carnap's and Bar-Hillel's sense; but he didn't bring up the fact that in information theory as in psychology you don't have information unless you have prior uncertainty. You have to consider the motivational state of the person to begin with, and then consider what he gets out of decisions in favor of alternative hypotheses.

FINCH: I agree heartily with Berlyne; I have myself recently offered in *Philosophy of Science*, October, 1960, a measure of the cognitive content of any proposition formulated as a product of a degree of confirmation and the log of prior probability—i.e., in "expectation" form. I have also found Sheckle's writings on surprise in decision-making very suggestive even in an information-theoretic context.

SELLARS: I would like to give an example which I think focuses the issue. If I come to a fork in the road, and I know (or have reason to believe) that one or the other of the roads will take me to New Haven, but the evidence is neutral as between the two hypotheses, and I want to get to New Haven and there is no other way, I may rationally choose to take the left-hand road. Yet I do not accept the hypothesis that the road goes to New Haven. It would, indeed, be irrational to do so. It seems perfectly clear that in this case there is a difference between acting on a hypothesis and accepting it. This simple kind of example ought to be explored before we go further.

BRAITHWAITE: The way in which utility and moral considerations enter into accepting a hypothesis are well illustrated in Sinclair Lewis' novel *Arrowsmith*. There the situation is that of the biologist doing a test on a vaccine which may be a cure for the plague. His problem is entirely concerned with the values involved: to release insufficiently tested vaccine; or to let people die. And we all heard Robbins' account of the wrong procedure, in an actual case, in accepting a hypothesis that batches of a vaccine were safe.

KYBURG: But the man in the laboratory is concerned with choosing one of two courses of action—he may like to think of himself as choosing between hypotheses, but the hypotheses do not really enter into his decision. He needs to choose between the actions of releasing a certain batch of vaccine or not releasing it. This is certainly not the same thing as accepting or rejecting a hypothesis.

JEFFREY: Although I agree that we accept hypotheses, I don't see that the acceptance of hypotheses has a simple relation to action. There is no single utility associated with general scientific hypotheses. Even in the vaccine case, the disutility to man and monkeys is not the same. Certainly, in the case of a general scientific hypothesis, there isn't any single utility or disutility; the utilities depend on what you are going to do with the hypothesis.

BRAITHWAITE: How we assign utilities does not matter; in Robbins' method, for example, the procedure is invariate with regard to any specific assignments of utilities.

BLACK: I don't believe anybody is prepared to say that there is *no* connection between belief and action. The interesting point that Sellars raised was a distinction between kinds of action. I would like to illustrate this by referring to his own example. I may rationally choose to take the left-hand fork because that has a better surface, knowing that on the evidence there is nothing to choose between the roads in terms of getting to New Haven. I am acting on the hypothesis, if you like, that the left-hand road is the correct one. But if someone were to ask me what was the way to New Haven, I would not say that the left-hand road is the way to go, whereas if I believed it, I certainly would say so. There's a difference in action; it's a difference in action appropriate to believing that the left-hand road goes there (which I don't) and acting as if it did (which I do).

BRAITHWAITE: You are misdescribing the choice of the smooth road when you say that you are choosing the hypothesis that it will take you to

New Haven. You are choosing the hypothesis that it is the smoother road. The hypotheses concerning which will take you to New Haven are, on the evidence, equally good.

SELLARS: But to choose to take the left-hand road on the ground that it is a *better* (because a smoother) road and that the evidence is neutral as to which road goes to New Haven, while it involves accepting the hypothesis that the road is smoother (and that the evidence is as it is), does not involve accepting the hypothesis that the road is the *right* one (because it goes to New Haven). In more complicated cases where there is both difference of utility and difference of likelihood, one may rationally *act on* a hypothesis which runs counter to the weight of the evidence. There is no absurdity in "I shall act on H_1 although H_2 is more likely."

*   *   *

LEVI: There is a confusion that goes through a good deal of the literature on decision theory between two kinds of decisions. There is a sense in which there is a decision involved in any kind of inductive inference: you decide to accept or to reject a hypothesis. Savage sometimes seems to suggest that when you decide to accept a hypothesis you're going to act on it relative to some objective; and then he shifts around and says that accepting a hypothesis is simply a decision. The same formal apparatus could be applicable to the two different types of decision problems. If so, it is still an open question whether the one problem can be reduced to the other, even though there is a trivial sense in which accepting a hypothesis is in itself a decision.

SELLARS: First there is a distinction in language between deciding *that p* and deciding to do A. Some cases of deciding *that p* can correctly be described as deciding to accept *p*. To accept *p* involves conditional decisions to act in various ways in various circumstances. This should not, however, blind us to the difference between deciding that *p* and deciding to do A. Again, any decision *that p* is likely to affirm at least some of the antecedents in such relevant conditional decisions to act as are dispositionally present in our minds. If it affirms the antecedent of such a conditional decision, it must nevertheless be carefully distinguished from the resulting categorical decision to act, to do A.

Second, Braithwaite misdescribed the situation which he said that we were misdescribing. If I take the left-hand road, seeing that the surface is better, what I am doing is incompletely described as taking the road with the better surface (which does imply that I am accepting the hypothesis on which I act). If there were a further road to the left marked "Hartford," with a still better surface, I would not take it.

It is surely clear that if I go on the better of the two roads, it is not *simply* because it has the better surface. I am acting on the hypothesis that the road goes to New Haven.

BAR-HILLEL: Accepting a hypothesis cannot be regarded as an action in any serious sense at all. I don't think accepting a hypothesis can be reduced to action. There does exist a partial reduction, in certain circumstances; but this is a matter that remains to be carefully investigated.

MORGENBESSER: May I make one further gloss on the road example? Suppose that both roads lead to New Haven, that they are equally well constructed, and so on. Now you choose the left-hand road, thus accepting the hypothesis that the left-hand road leads to New Haven. Aren't you thereby rejecting the hypothesis that the right-hand road leads to New Haven?

BRAITHWAITE: I'm not making any commitment about the right-hand road at all.

* * *

MORGENBESSER: Why is rejection of a universal hypothesis by a single negative instance independent of utility considerations?

BRAITHWAITE: Because, by such an instance, the hypothesis is refuted by the evidence. Deciding to accept or reject is more than acting at the moment; it is a matter also of developing better dispositions to act on successive occasions.

FINCH: I have often wondered why Braithwaite takes as a paradigm of universal law the statement, "Every instance of beta properties is an instance of alpha properties," without allowing for metricized predicates. Universal metricized laws in the sciences have statistical hypotheses as implicates, and have since the time of Gauss been so treated. Hence the acceptability of universal laws is in principle subject to any technique of induction utilizing likelihoods of observations—i.e., probability of deviations in measurements—for it is surely the case that the acceptability of any hypothesis is not unrelated to the acceptability of its implicates.

* * *

BAR-HILLEL: There is no theoretical refutation of Braithwaite's position regarding the arbitrary choice of hypotheses. An agent who changes his a priori probabilities or seriosities from day to day so as to rationalize his choices cannot be theoretically refuted. His behavior will indeed be unpredictable and thus no doubt he will get into trouble with other people; but this is not a logical refutation. I cannot even say that he behaves "irrationally."

KYBURG: I am surprised that Bar-Hillel finds that beliefs that we would call "irrational" in any ordinary sense of the word cannot be theoretically refuted. Perhaps there hasn't been enough theory developed yet to provide a refutation. But it seems too strong to me to say that these beliefs *cannot* be refuted. I think we ought to strive to find that logical structure which will allow us to refute this degree of arbitrariness, because it seems to me that we all know perfectly well that the person who is readjusting his probabilities every morning is just plain irrational.

BAR-HILLEL: You are stretching the term "logical" beyond the sense in which a formal logician likes to use it. Do you identify "logical" with rational"?

BLACK: Since we want to go as far as possible with rational justification, we would not be satisfied with a random assignment of prior probabilities. We wouldn't be nearly satisfied with a system of statistical inference in which the choice of a priori probabilities was not merely arbitrary, but could shift in completely random ways. We do really need, if we can find it, some way of rendering this choice more determinate.

SELLARS: It seems to me that the "initial probability" carries with it a burden which is such that we cannot speak of simply "choosing" it.

LEVI: The coherence of seriosities requires further analysis of personal probability and utility. To establish coherence—in Savage's sense—wouldn't we have to analyze seriosities into probabilities and utilities? As it stands, Braithwaite doesn't take this step.

BRAITHWAITE: My moral philosophy is ideal-utilitarian. I do not believe in doing everything with utilities. Methods invariant for all utilities—such as, perhaps, those involving personal probabilities—can and ought to be sought.

Epilogue

W<small>E</small> hope that this is not a real epilogue, for we hope that this conference has not come to a conclusion, and will not come to one in the future. The most important fact about the conference is that it not only represents the meeting and mingling of a number of lines of thought, but that these lines of thought, these approaches to various aspects of the problems of induction, do not come to an end at the nexus represented by our conference, but continue into the future. It is our hope and expectation, of course, that they will not continue unchanged; we hope that they will have been modified by their brief contact with other lines of thought and other approaches to similar problems.

These expectations have not been completely fulfilled, of course; if one's hopes were not beyond complete fulfilment, one would run the dreadful risk of finding oneself altogether satisfied. The most serious shortcoming of the meeting was the lack of contact (of interchange of effects) among representatives of different disciplines. One reason for this is the fact that the conference committee, being composed mainly of philosophers, had difficulty finding speakers in other disciplines and arousing their interest. Perhaps in the future, now that this conference has been held, it will be easier to get a broader representation among such disciplines as sociology, psychology, physics, etc. But another reason for lack of effective contact is simply the vast intellectual depths that separate the professional in one discipline from the professional in another, even when they seem to use many of the same concepts.

There are a number of stages through which people pass in attempting to cross over these depths. The first stage is that of rather complete ignorance: the professor of A is an out-and-out beginner when it comes to B, and may not even know that A and B have many terms and concepts in common. The next stage is generally a delightful one: A and B discover that their professional languages overlap. They have a small area of technical language in common, and this suggests connections between the fields. One reaction to this is to go off half-cocked—and this reaction is by no means always the least fruitful: the professor of A can use his undisciplined, half-understood, amateur knowledge of B as a source of inspiration. He may write impressionistic nonsense about B, while at the same time using this impressionistic nonsense as a springboard for profound and fundamental results in his own field of A. Another reaction, a more scholarly one, is to take the other fellow's discipline more seriously still, and to try to see if the disciplines overlap as much as the vocabularies. This course leads, initially, to disappointment. The more carefully the discpilines are studied, the clearer it becomes that their vocabularies do not overlap as much as was thought; the same words are used, but the meanings are different. The stage of complete disillusionment sets in, however, when it is discovered that the problems that the two disciplines are attacking are not even the same problems—they may turn out to be problems of a completely different sort, even though the words used to describe them may be the same, and even if the methods of attacking them are somewhat the same.

Fortunately there is a stage beyond this one; where it is realized that although the problems are not the same, and although the vocabularies do not have as many meanings in common as they have words, and although the methodologies of the two disciplines may be completely different, still, the meeting and mingling of the two disciplines may be highly fruitful, and may have offspring which, however unorthodox their parentage, can contribute greatly to the one real intellectual discipline: the quest for knowledge and understanding. Such offspring are rare, of course; but conjugation between two professions may still be profitable and pleasurable in the absence of the expectation of a single large contribution. It may even be that in the large sum, and on the whole, the small contacts at this tolerant stage of mutual understanding and respect make a larger contribution to the total of human understanding than the more noticeable synthetic products of interdisciplinary relations.

At any event, we have certainly made strides in the direction of mutual understanding and respect at this meeting, even though this may also be the direction in which we still have furthest to go. It is certainly the case that without this understanding we cannot hope to understand the world, or even our own disciplines, as well as we would like or as well as we should.

It has already been noted that no summing up of the results of this conference is possible, simply because it wasn't that sort of conference. It is also difficult to sum up the reactions of the participants, even though the primary object of the conference was precisely to stimulate those reactions. Any statement about the reactions will be largely personal and private. It will be best, perhaps, and give as clear an idea of the tenor of the reactions as possible, if we simply quote the explicit reactions of two of the conference participants. The two quotations have the same source: on the last day of the conference several of the participants were asked to give their reactions; these are excerpts from two of the most provocative statements.

H. E. K., Jr.

Final Impressions

By D. E. Berlyne

I FEEL great hesitation about imparting my impressions of the conference. This is not because they are predominantly unfavorable. On the contrary, it has been an instructive and much appreciated privilege to participate in discussions with such a distinguished company. It is simply that the impressions of one who is not trained or professionally engaged in philosophy must of necessity be ignorant impressions. Nevertheless, mine have been asked for, and the only function a non-philosopher can perform in a group like this is to present his reactions, however naïve, in the hope that they may be of some interest.

I have, first of all, been fascinated throughout the conference by the differences between the ways in which philosophical and psychological discussions are conducted. It is not that I mean to be critical, and the last thing I should want to do is to hold up psychologists as a model in this respect. But often during the past week it has not been clear to me exactly what speakers were aiming to achieve and how they expected to know when they had achieved it. There is a famous story about the Duke of Wellington, who was present when a certain general had an arm carried off by a cannon ball. The Duke said, "By Gad, you've lost an arm!", and the general replied, "By Gad, you're right, sir!" When I asked myself what your criterion of validity was, it seemed often to be something like an expectation that, if somebody arrived at a correct view of induction, his colleagues would leap to their feet, thump their palms, and exclaim "By Gad, you're right, sir!" But the history of philosophy suggests that such exclamations do not occur with much unanimity and shows that, when philosophers are moved to say, "By Gad, you're right sir!" they are apt to say, "By Gad, you're wrong, sir!" a generation later.

The average experimental psychologist, while he is certainly not a paragon of methodological sophistication, is trained to be explicit about his aims and his criteria of validity. He is ready to be challenged at any point to make clear exactly what it is that he is asserting; how he and everybody else can know that he is right; and, if he does not know, what could be done to find out whether he is right. This is largely due to the influence of a certain kind of philosophy of science which is, I understand, no longer as prevalent as it once was.

To turn to the question of what role the behavioral sciences might play in discussions of induction, there is, first of all, no doubt that philosophical problems can be defined in such a way that psychological and other empirical considerations have no bearing on them whatsoever. It is clearly possible, if one insists, to discuss induction without reference to how people induce, just as logical discussion can be, and customarily is, carried on without reference to how people actually think, and mathematical discussion is carried on without reference to any physical phenomena that might interpret a mathematical system. In the cases of logic and mathematics, however, the aims of the discussion, the criteria of validity, and the reasons for conducting the discussion in that way are clearly laid down.

Nevertheless, there are many obvious ways in which it might be illuminating for philosophers, behavioral scientists, and others to collaborate in building up an integrated account of induction that benefits from the multiplicity of their points of view and contributed experience. For one thing, philosophers do not in practice leave out empirical, including psychological, considerations when discussing matters like induction. Time and again during the past week, somebody has expressed misgivings about a particular position on the grounds that it is not "convincing" or that it does not reflect the nature of actual scientific research. Yet psychologists know from the early history of their discipline and from their own professional experience how dangerous it is to make statements about a complex form of behavior like scientific research on the basis of a few illustrative anecdotes, or to believe that the introspective observation of one's own reactions will reveal how satisfying or dissatisfying something will be for the human intellect in general. Individual differences and the possibilities of misperception are much greater than anybody who has not had a training in psychology can realize. To support empirical statements about psychological or sociological phenomena, elaborate and sophisticated techniques of data-collection, such as those that the behavioral sciences have developed, are indispensable. Some partisans of a "humane studies" approach refuse to accept this. They are generally persons who admit with pride that their education did not include the behavioral sciences. It is hard to believe that it included history !

It is surely impossible to arrive at anything that can be called an "understanding" of induction without combining solutions to the philosophical, logical, mathematical, and empirical problems raised by induction. Discussion of induction may, if one insists, be carried on in a vacuum, but induction and the problems of induction did not grow out of a vacuum but out of a network of biological and psychological circumstances. Human beings have presumably been inducing since their species first appeared, because of the needs imposed on them by their internal, geographical, and social environments, and because they have emerged from the rough-and-tumble of evolution with equipment that enables them to do so. This equipment bears some resemblances to equipment possessed by lower animals that makes them capable of immeasurably simpler analogues of induction. Surely, any view of induction that deliberately ignores these facts is incomplete and therefore deceptive.

Then there is the behavior of discussing and particularly of justifying induction, which is itself an interesting and therefore instructive phenomenon. How did it grow up? It did not grow up because ordinary men or practicing scientists have hesitations about using induction, although they might hope for guidance toward better ways of inducing as an outcome of philosophical analysis. But there have for a long time been men of a particular cast of mind who have been sensitive to problems pertaining to induction and willing to devote great efforts to seeking descriptions of induction that will resolve these problems. What is there about the human nervous system that disturbs it so potently when it contemplates something like induction after undergoing a certain kind of education? It might, one could imagine, be easier to see how these conceptual discomforts are to be relieved if one first knew more about their roots. I must make it clear that what I am thinking of here is not a personality-assessment or psychoanalytic explanation of why a particular individual is abnormally persistent in pursuing particular problems. Although most members of the human race spend little if any time reflecting about induction, concern over such problems must stem from some universal characteristics of the human organism, as must the capacity to recognize, and be gratified by, rational solutions to them.

Although representatives of studies other than philosophy were outnumbered at this conference, we had a sufficient variety of personnel to provide a rare opportunity for fresh looks at induction derived from an interdisciplinary synthesis. I, for one, very much regretted that such new approaches to very old problems were not explored.

Final Impressions
By BLACK

I am inclined to take as a text a remark that William James once made which has always appealed to me: "What should we conclude when nothing has been concluded?" I myself do not regard this as a criticism; I'd be rather skeptical if after a week of this sort people had changed their minds radically, or felt that conclusions had been reached. The point has obviously not been to reach conclusions, but to find an opportunity which is all too rare of meeting other thinkers as persons, of getting something of the feel of their ideas. In my judgment the most important things in this conference won't appear in the conference book, and will be highly intangible.

Somewhat to my surprise, I find that the large questions that have arisen (and here perhaps I disagree with Mr. Berlyne) have been on the whole methodological questions. I'm interested in this because—perhaps through simple-mindedness or dogmatism—I think that these questions really do have answers, and that the real difficulties of the subject lie elsewhere. The lack of agreement about them may reflect a lack of common background rather than any intrinsic difficulty in the questions themselves.

The first large question is: What problems are we really discussing? While I quite agree with Mr. Berlyne that there must be all kinds of interesting empirical questions about, e.g., the behavior of people drawing statistical inferences, the construction of machines, and so on, it seems to me that, by and large, the people here have not been discussing those questions. They have come up in a different capacity, in order to throw light on the problems we have been discussing. I would say that these problems are the problems of elaborating, explaining, inventing, justifying the rationale of non-deductive inference. If one thinks, for instance, of the classical discussion of Mill in the *System of Logic*, and sets that against the kind of thing that Mr. Braithwaite was offering to us, the contrast is very striking, and I can't help thinking very much to the credit of our generation. It seems to me that whatever enormous problems remain unsolved, we have gone a long distance in replacing simple-minded and ultimately not very interesting questions by complicated and on the whole rather interesting and fruitful ones.

The second large question (one that Mr. Berlyne said a good many things about a few minutes ago) is the relation in this kind of inquiry between empirical and non-empirical inquiry. Now I suppose that there must be a certain sort of connection between the two kinds of inquiry. Even the most subjective defender or rationalizer of non-deductive inference is appealing to some kind of consensus. That is to say, I suppose there are facts about the ways that people argue; and if one is ignorant about those facts, then the non-empirical discussion will proceed in the void. To this extent I am fully in agreement with Mr. Berlyne, and I fully agree with him that it is folly just to ignore facts which bear upon questions of non-deductive inference. Now where I disagree with him is on the issue of whether psychology and the social sciences generally have, at this moment, a great deal to offer. I have tried to follow and be instructed by the work of psychologists, and I must say that I've learned a great deal from them. What I don't find, I'm sorry to say, is that I get any help in my philosophical questions; I just don't get philosophical help from psychology in its present state. One reason for this is that psychology is just at the beginning of things, and quite properly is dealing with highly simplified questions first. If an extremely simplified situation is set up, for good scientific reason, the very simplicity of the experiment may add to its empirical usefulness but detract from its philosophical interest.

This brings me to the third and the last of the large questions. I think a number of persons here have been troubled by the question: What is philosophical method? I think I detect in Mr. Berlyne the idea that it's either psychology or, if not, it ought to be. Or rather, put it this way: If it isn't logic, then perhaps it ought to be psychology; what is there in between? Now I don't think this is an enormous mystery. Philosophers have been engaged—and not only professional philosophers by any means—in clarifying concepts for a long time; and I think we could produce good examples of cases where the investigation of a concept by a philosopher has produced a certain kind of illumination and insight, sometimes in a way which has been of direct relevance to science itself. This is not an empirical method at all. It's what we laymen call *thinking*, and that is not a method of inquiry. It is neither empirical nor, strictly speaking, logical. So I would suggest that this sharp contrast between the logical and the empirical is itself something which ought to be by this time outmoded. I agree with Mr. Berlyne that the analytic-synthetic distinction is too crude, but perhaps we ought to think now of the contrast between logic and empirical science as artificial.

If we look at the writings of Mr. Braithwaite, as an example, I think we could find instance after instance where he is no longer doing mathematics or logic but is doing philosophy and is now raising questions about the meaning of action, decision, belief, theory; these are the sorts of questions I have in mind.

There are still differences in method among philosophers, and I think some of these differences have appeared this week. There are philosophers who prefer to work, deliberately, with idealized models: Mr. Carnap has been quoted very often this week. He offers a prime example of it, in his approach to probability theory. So far as I can see, this is a thoroughly respectable method.

It seems to me that the new wave of this extremely complicated and interesting subject is what I am going to call, borrowing Braithwaite's term, the praxeological approach. The shift to policies seems to me to have produced an important and even a dramatic change in the subject. There are people who say that this is just a shift in terminology—that, basically speaking, the very same questions you get in confirmation theory will turn up. But I don't believe this myself. I think that, partly for historic reasons, the development of the theory of decisions, game theory, information theory, and so on has encouraged people to go into this line of country. It is extremely promising. I think (and I'm sure that Braithwaite would agree with me) that it is also extremely difficult. There are on the one hand technical questions which are very far from being solved; so that, even on the mathematical and logical side, the theory of games, the theory of statistical inference, seem to me still in their lusty infancy. Therefore I count Mr. Robbins' paper one of the most exciting things that happened this week, because I saw there a glimpse of this subject developing.

On the other side, it seems to me that there are clearly very difficult conceptual problems connected with the praxeological approach which have hardly begun to be properly discussed. It is not at all clear what "accepting" means, what "choosing" means, what "believing" means. Philosophers, of course, have talked about these things for many centuries, but they haven't talked about them in quite this kind of context. They have assumed a highly contemplative, reflective context. And they have pushed these questions into a limbo of practical reason. It seems to me very interesting that (if I may use the old-fashioned word) practical reason is becoming respectable, and that philosophers and logicians as well as game theorists and philosophers of science are now prepared to make a serious effort to sharpen our conceptual apparatus in this field. So, speaking for myself, this is what I have learned from the conference: the great promises and the great desirability of further work in this praxeological area.

Participants in the 1961 Wesleyan Conference on Induction

Alan Anderson
Yale University

Myron Anderson
Trinity College

W. Ross Ashby★
Burden Neurological Institute

Yehoshua Bar-Hillel
Hebrew University

Stephen Barker
Swarthmore College

Max Black
Cornell University

Daniel E. Berlyne
Boston University

Henry Bohm
Wayne State University

Richard B. Braithwaite
Cambridge University

Peter Caws
University of Kansas

Robert S. Cohen
Boston University

Jack Cowan
Massachusetts Institute of Technology

Henry Finch
Pennsylvania State University

Adolf Grünbaum
University of Pittsburgh

Norwood Russell Hanson★
Indiana University

Richard C. Jeffrey
Stanford University

William Kessen
Yale University

Arnold Koslow
Columbia University

Cornelius Krusé
Wesleyan University

Henry E. Kyburg, Jr.
Wesleyan University

Hugues Leblanc
Bryn Mawr College

John W. Lenz
Brown University

Isaac Levi
Western Reserve University

Warren McCulloch
Massachusetts Institute of Technology

Edward Madden
San José State College

Leonard Meyer
University of Chicago

Harlan Mills
Mathematica

Louis Mink
Wesleyan University

Sidney Morgenbesser
Columbia University

Ernest Nagel
Columbia University

F. S. C. Northrop
Yale University

Nello Onesto
University of Rome

★ Contributed paper, unable to appear because of illness

Paul Reynolds
Wesleyan University

Herbert Robbins
Columbia University

Wesley C. Salmon
Brown University

Michael Scriven
Indiana University

Wilfrid Sellars
Yale University

Paul L. Shiman
Wesleyan University

Howard Smokler
Rutgers University

Harry Tartar
City College of New York

Leo A. M. Verbieck
The Hague, Netherlands

Philip Weiner
City College of New York

William Weedon
University of Virginia

Notes on Contributors

W. Ross Ashby, director of the Burden Neurological Institute to 1960, is professor in the Department of Electrical Engineering, University of Illinois. He is president of the Society for General Systems Theory and Research, and is a member of the Council of the International Association of Cybernetics. He is author of more than seventy scientific papers, and his books include *Design for a Brain* and *An Introduction to Cybernetics.*

Daniel E. Berlyne is associate professor of psychology at the University of Toronto. Besides articles in various British and American journals, his publications include *Conflict, Arousal and Curiosity*; *Structure and Direction in Thinking*; and (in collaboration with J. Piaget) *Théorie du comportement et opérations.*

R. B. Braithwaite, f.b.a., is Knightsbridge Professor of Moral Philosophy, Cambridge University. He is president of the British Society for the Philosophy of Science. His most recent publications include contributions to the symposia *Observation and Interpretation* and *The Axiomatic Method*; his principal books are *Scientific Explanation, Theory of Games as a Tool for the Moral Philosopher*, and *An Empiricist's View of the Nature of Religious Belief.*

Adolf Grünbaum, Andrew Mellon Professor of Philosophy at the University of Pittsburgh, is vice-president of the American Association for the Advancement of Science. He is a member of the editorial board of *Philosophy of Science* and has contributed many articles to that and other journals. His most recent book is *Philosophical Problems of Space and Time.*

Norwood Russell Hanson is professor of philosophy and chairman of the Department of History and Logic of Science at Indiana University. His many distinctions include Fulbright, Ford, Rockefeller, and Nuffield Foundation fellowships—also the D.F.C. and Air Medal, won as a Marine Corps fighter pilot. Among his more than eighty articles and books are *The Concept of the Positron* and *Explanation and Prediction in the History of Planetary Theory.*

Henry E. Kyburg, Jr., assistant professor of mathematics at Wesleyan when the conference recorded in these pages took place, is associate professor of philosophy at the University of Denver. He has contributed articles to the *Journal of Philosophy*, the *Review of Mathematics*, the *British Journal for the Philosophy of Science*, and other periodicals. His book *Probability and the Logic of Rational Belief* appeared in 1961.

HUGUES LEBLANC is professor of philosophy at Bryn Mawr. His published works include *An Introduction to Deductive Logic*, *Logica Mathematica*, and *Statistical and Inductive Probabilities*. His contribution to the present symposium derives in part from the last-named monograph.

SIDNEY MORGENBESSER, associate professor of philosophy at Columbia University, is book review editor of the *Journal of Philosophy*. His publications include articles in that periodical and elsewhere. He is co-editor (with Arthur J. Danto) of *Readings in Philosophy of Science* and (with J. Walsh) of *Freedom of the Will*.

ERNEST NAGEL has been associated with Columbia University since 1931; he is now John Dewey Professor of Philosophy. Among his many publications are *The Logic of Measurement*, *Introduction to Logic and Scientific Methods* (with Morris R. Cohen), *Principles of the Theory of Probability*, *Sovereign Reason*, *Logic Without Metaphysics*, and most recently *The Structure of Science*.

HERBERT E. ROBBINS is professor of mathematical statistics at Columbia. He has written many articles on probability and statistics, and is co-author (with Richard Courant) of *What Is Mathematics?*

WESLEY C. SALMON, associate professor of philosophy at Brown University, is a research fellow at the Minnesota Center for the Philosophy of Science for spring 1963. He has contributed papers on induction to various journals and to the volume *Current Issues in the Philosophy of Science*, edited by Feigl and Maxwell. His most recent book is *Logic*, published in the Prentice-Hall Foundations of Philosophy series.

Index